Classworks
Numeracy

Series editors

Len and Anne Frobisher

Author team

Len Frobisher, Anne Frobisher

John Taylor, John Spooner, Thelma Page

Ray Steele, Mike Spooner, Anitra Vickery

Contents

Introduction

What this book contains

- Visual resources for structuring mental, written and problem-solving work.

- Examples of modelled mathematical methods and solutions.

- Lesson ideas including key questions and plenary support.

- Photocopiable pages to aid and structure pupil work.

- Blocked units to slot into medium-term planning.

- Oral/mental starter ideas to complement the daily teaching of mental facts and skills.

- Every idea is brief, to the point, and on one page.

How this book is organised

- There are blocked units of work from one week to several, depending on the strand.

- Each blocked unit is organised into a series of chunks of teaching content.

- Each 'chunk' has accompanying suggestions for visual modelling of teaching.

- For many teaching ideas we supply photocopiable resources.

- The objectives covered in the units are based on DfES sample medium-term planning.

- The units are organised in strand-based chunks, in a suggested order for teaching.

Planning a unit of work

How to incorporate *Classworks* material into your medium-term plan

- Pick the most relevant unit for what you want to teach – the units are organised in strands, sequentially according to the DfES sample medium-term plans.

- To find the content, look at the objectives on the first page of every unit.

- Or just browse through by topic, picking out the ideas you want to adapt.

- Every page has its content clearly signalled so you can pick and choose.

- Choose a generic starter from the bank at the back of the book if required.

What each page does

Learning outcome clearly signalled

Objectives spelt out

Key mathematical concepts listed

Shaded sections refer to *Classworks* ideas, white sections to suggested extra content or just space for your notes

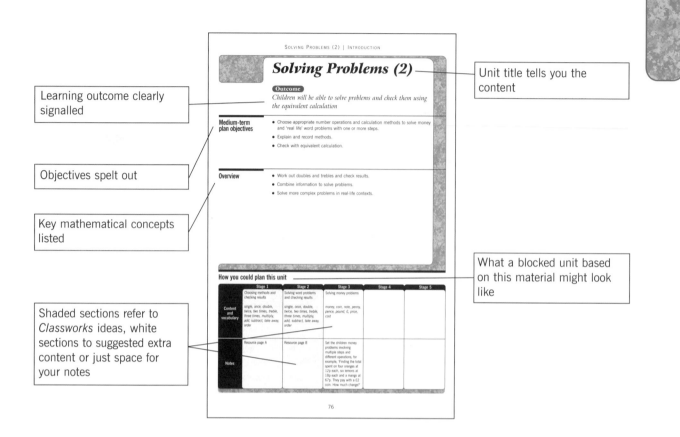

Unit title tells you the content

What a blocked unit based on this material might look like

Clear headings for each section of the page

Main idea broken up into bullets and key questions

Brief independent, paired or group work idea

Plenary guidance

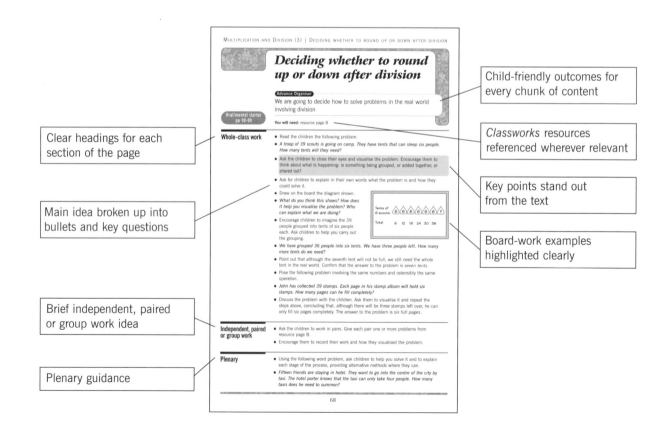

Child-friendly outcomes for every chunk of content

Classworks resources referenced wherever relevant

Key points stand out from the text

Board-work examples highlighted clearly

Properties of Number (1)

Outcome

Children will be able to use their knowledge of the number system to estimate and read scales

Medium-term plan objectives	• Read and write whole numbers to 10,000 in figures and words. • Know what each digit represents and partition numbers into Th, H, T, U. • Read and write the vocabulary of estimation. • Estimate up to 250 objects. • Estimate a proportion (fraction). • Read scales to a suitable degree of accuracy.
Overview	• Make, read and partition four-digit numbers. • Say the value of any digit in a four-digit number. • Estimate the number of objects in a full container. • Estimate the proportion of a container that is partly full. • Estimate the position of a number on an undivided number line.

How you could plan this unit

	Stage 1	Stage 2	Stage 3	Stage 4	Stage 5
Content and vocabulary	Partitioning four-digit numbers *4-digit number, thousands, hundreds, tens, units*	Estimating how many *estimate, proportion, container*	Estimating numbers on a number line *approximate, estimate, number line*		
Notes			Resource page A		

Partitioning four-digit numbers

Oral/mental starter
p 183

Advance Organiser

We are going to make four-digit numbers

You will need: large digit cards, 2, 5, 7 and 8; multiple of 1000, 100, 10 and 1 cards; 0 to 9 number cards (one set per child)

Whole-class work

5	7	2	8

- Use the large digit cards 2, 5, 7 and 8.

- Invite four children to the front of the class.

- Give each child one of the digit cards to make a four-digit number, say 5728.

- *Read this number for me.*

- Ask the children to explain why this is called a four-digit number. Give the children cards for multiples of 1000, 100, 10 and 1.

- Point at random to each digit the children are holding up in turn.

- *Hold up the number card that shows the value of this digit.*

- Ask the children to explain how they decided on the value of each digit.

- Ask the four children to make a different number with the 2, 5, 7 and 8 digits.

- Repeat the activity.

- Choose another four children.

- Invite the class to say a four-digit number that uses the same four digits.

- The children at the front of the class have to make the number.

- Repeatedly change the children at the front so that everyone has a turn.

Independent, paired or group work

- Children work in pairs. Each child has a set of 0 to 9 number cards.

- One child chooses any four digits to make a four-digit number (for example, 3508). This is recorded by each as 3508 = 3000 + 500 + 0 + 8.

- This is repeated until all numbers are completed.

- Children then reverse the activity and repeat 3000 + 500 + 0 + 8 = ____ .

Plenary

- Challenge the children to use their 0 to 9 digit cards to make a 4-digit number that has 3 hundreds.

- Invite them to tell you their number. Record each number on the board.

- Extend this to numbers that have: 3 thousands and 0 units; 7 tens, 1 hundred and 9 thousands; 4 units, 2 thousands, 5 hundreds and 8 tens.

Estimating how many

Advance Organiser

We are going to estimate the number of objects in a container

**Oral/mental starter
p 183**

You will need: a box of paper clips, a jar of marbles, a bag of cubes, a pile of coins, other small objects to estimate

Whole-class work

- Write a table on the board, like the one opposite, ready to show the children.

- Show the children the box of paper clips. Rattle the box and show them one paper clip.

- *How many paper clips do you think there are in the box?*

Objects	Estimates	Correct number
Box of paper clips Jar of marbles Bag of cubes Pile of coins		

- Remind them that they are making estimates and that when estimating it is sensible to use rounded numbers.

- Record some of the estimates on the table.

- Discuss how sensible the estimates are.

- *Are there more than ten paper clips? Are there fewer than 1000? What is a more sensible estimate?*

- Together, count the paper clips in sets of ten and then find how many there are in total.

- Compare the correct number with the estimates.

Independent, paired or group work

- Ask the children to work in pairs using sets of objects as in the table. Each pair has a few minutes to agree on an estimate – they can either estimate *about 200* or *more than 150 but less than 300*.

- Each pair records their estimate and then passes the set of objects to another pair.

Plenary

- Show the children each set of objects in turn and take estimates from the pairs.

- Discuss the differences with the children and why they might occur.

- On the board, write any tips the children have for estimating.

- *Who did anything differently?*

- Demonstrate or ask the children to help you count the objects and then discuss how close the estimates were.

- *What was easier to estimate? What was more difficult? Why do you think that is?*

Estimating numbers on a number line

Advance Organiser

We are going to find numbers on a number line

Oral/mental starter
p 183

You will need: large number line; number cards 0, 5, 10, 100; card arrowheads; resource page A (one per child)

Whole-class work

- Show the children a large, unmarked number line. Place 0 and 10 number cards in the boxes.

- Establish that the children understand that 0 and 10 are positions on the line and that there are numbers between 0 and 10.
- *What do the arrows indicate at each end of the number line?*
- Place an arrow at approximately 7.

- *What whole number is the arrow pointing to?*
- Discuss how the children decided.
- Explain that when making estimates of numbers on a number line it is helpful to find the 'middle' number.
- Invite a child, say Claire, to point to the position of the middle number.
- *What number is Claire pointing to? How did you work it out?*
- Place a 5 number card in its approximate position.

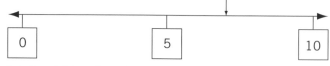

- Ask the children how this could help them decide that the arrow is pointing to 7.
- Move the arrow to other whole number positions.
- Repeat the activity with a 0 to 100 number line. In this case, you may wish to encourage children to mark the approximate positions of the multiples of 10 to help them estimate the number the arrow is pointing to.

Independent, paired or group work

- Ask the children to complete resource page A.

Plenary

- Go through the children's work on resource page A and discuss the different methods used.

PUPIL PAGE

Estimating numbers on a line

Write in the numbers the arrows are pointing to.

Name: _____

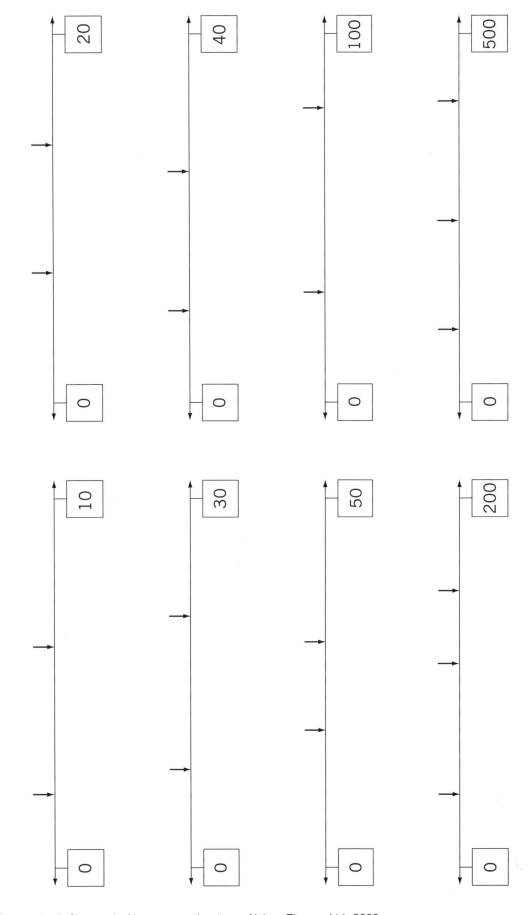

Properties of Number (2)

Outcome

Children will be able to extend number patterns and investigate statements about numbers

Medium-term plan objectives	• Recognise and extend number sequences formed by counting from any number in steps of a constant size; for example, count on in steps of 25 to 500.
	• Recognise odd and even numbers up to 1000 and some of their properties; for example, the outcome of sums or differences of pairs of odd/even numbers.
	• Solve number puzzles, recognise patterns, generalise and predict.
Overview	• Extend number sequences and find their rule.
	• Make general statements about numbers that are 1 more and 1 less than odd and even numbers.
	• Use a systematic approach to solve number puzzles.

How you could plan this unit

	Stage 1	Stage 2	Stage 3	Stage 4	Stage 5
Content and vocabulary	Extending sequences and finding rules *sequence, extend, rule, predict*	1 more and 1 less than even and odd numbers *sorting diagram, odd/even numbers, 1 more/less*	Solving number puzzles *sum, difference, product*		
Notes			Resource page A		

Extending sequences and finding rules

Advance Organiser

We are going to find rules for sequences

You will need: number cards 0 to 50

Whole-class work

- On the board, use number cards to show the sequence 1, 4, 7, 10, 13, 16, 19 with the 1 card showing its number and the rest showing the blank side.

- Explain that you are thinking of a number sequence and the children have to predict what the next number will be each time.

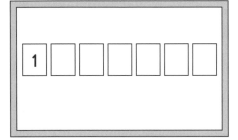

- *What is the next number after 1 in my sequence?*

- Turn over the 4 when the correct number is given.

- Repeat for each of the other numbers.

- Discuss how to find a few more numbers in the sequence.

- Establish that 3 is added each time to a number to find the next number.

- Build up the addition between each pair of numbers, as shown.

- Tell the children that we say '+ 3' is the rule for this sequence.

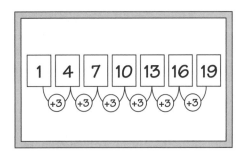

- Repeat the activity for the sequence 32, 28, 24, 20, 16, 12, 8 which has the rule '− 4'.

Independent, paired or group work

- Ask the children to complete similar diagrams to explain the following number patterns:
51, 45, 39, 33; 89, 98, 107, 116; 152, 164, 176, 188;
227, 215, 203, 191; 475, 500, 525, 550.

Plenary

- Ask each child to write their own secret sequence.

- Invite a child to write the start of their sequence on the board. Have the rest of the class guess what the numbers in the sequence are and what the rule is.

- The child who first guesses the rule comes to the board to show their sequence.

1 more and 1 less than even and odd numbers

Advance Organiser

We are going to make general statements about odd and even numbers

Oral/mental starter p 183

You will need: number cards 138, 674 and 952

Whole-class work

- Draw this sorting diagram on the board.
- Hold up the number card 138.
- *Is 138 an odd number or an even number? How can you tell?*
- Discuss the odd nature of the tens and hundreds digits and that it is only the unit digit that decides whether a number is odd or even.

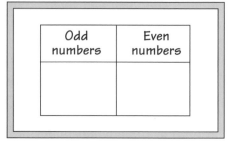

- *Where should I write 138 in the sorting diagram?* Write *138* in the 'even' column.
- *What number is 1 more than 138?*
- *Is 139 odd or even? Where should I write 139 in the sorting diagram?*
- *What number is 1 less than 138?*
- *Is 137 odd or even? Where should I write 137 in the sorting diagram?*
- Record *137*, *138* and *139* on the board.
- Repeat the activity for the even numbers 952 and 674.
- Ask the children to make a general statement about numbers that are 1 more and 1 less than an even number.
- Write on the board: *The numbers that are 1 more than and 1 less than an even number are odd numbers.*

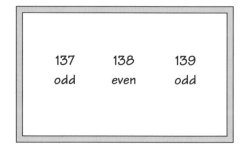

- Remind the children that this is a general statement because it does not use particular numbers.

Independent, paired or group work

- Ask the children to investigate the statement above, in pairs.
- Encourage them to choose another number and repeat.

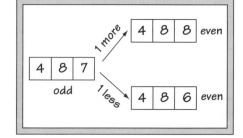

Plenary

- Ask the children how they could investigate making a general statement about numbers that are 2 more and 2 less than an even number and what they think the statement would be.
- Use some examples of three-digit even numbers to support the general statement, *The numbers that are 2 more and 2 less than an even number are even.*

Solving number puzzles

Oral/mental starter p 183

Advance Organiser

We are going to solve number puzzles

You will need: resource page A (one per child)

Whole-class work

- Write on the board the following number puzzle: *I am thinking of two numbers. The sum of the numbers is 10 and the product of the two numbers is 16. What are my two numbers?*

- Invite the children to find your two numbers.

- Discuss the methods they used.

- Explain that you are going to show them a systematic method of finding two numbers in a number puzzle like this.

- Rewrite the puzzle on the board as: *I am thinking of two numbers. The sum of the numbers is 10 and the product of the two numbers is 24. What are my two numbers?*

- Explain that as they do not know the two numbers, it is helpful to give them letters, such as A and B.

- Discuss with the children how they think a table can be used to find the two numbers A and B.

- *Tell me two numbers that have a sum of 10.*

- From the different suggestions choose 9 and 1.

- Discuss that choosing 9 and 1, to start with, is a systematic approach. Build up the rest of the first two columns.

- *What is the product of 9 and 1?*

- Repeat for the other pairs of numbers.

- When 6 and 4 is reached some children will not wish to go any further. Explain that it is important to complete the table as a different pair of numbers may also have a product of 24.

Number A	Number B	Sum of A and B	Product of A and B
9	1	10	9
8	2	10	16
7	3	10	21
6	4	10	24
5	5	10	25
4	6	10	24
3	7	10	21
2	8	10	16
1	9	10	9

Independent, paired or group work

- Ask the children to complete resource page A.

Plenary

- Work through the examples on resource page A.

- You may wish to show how knowledge of sums and differences of odd and even numbers can reduce the number of pairs that are tested.

(**PUPIL PAGE**)

Name: _____

Solving number problems

The sum of two numbers is 12.
The product of the two numbers is 35.
What are the two numbers?

Number A	Number B	Sum of A and B	Product of A and B

The sum of two numbers is 14.
The product of the two numbers is 48.
What are the two numbers?

Number A	Number B	Sum of A and B	Product of A and B

The difference of two numbers is 6.
The product of the two numbers is 27.
What are the two numbers?

Number A	Number B	Difference of A and B	Product of A and B

Classworks © Classworks Numeracy author team, Nelson Thornes Ltd, 2003

Properties of Number (3)

Outcome

Children will be able to use partitioning to compare numbers, using the appropriate symbols

Medium-term plan objectives	
	● Multiply and divide any integer up to 1000 by 10 and understand the effect.
	● Read and write the vocabulary of comparing and ordering numbers.
	● Use symbols =, <, > correctly.
	● Give a number lying between two numbers.
	● Use vocabulary of approximation.
	● Round any positive number less than 1000 to nearest 10.
	● Recognise negative numbers in context; for example, on a number line, thermometer.

Overview	
	● Multiply a three-digit number by 10.
	● Divide a three-digit multiple of 10 by 10.
	● Use the symbols < and > when relating to numbers less than 1000.

How you could plan this unit

	Stage 1	Stage 2	Stage 3	Stage 4	Stage 5
Content and vocabulary	Multiply and divide by 10 *expanded notation, multiply by 10, divide by 10, general statement*	Introducing the < and the > symbols *< symbol or sign, > symbol or sign, less than, more than, inequality statement*	Using the < and the > symbols *< symbol or sign, > symbol or sign, less than, more than, inequality statement*		
Notes	Resource page A				

11

Multiply and divide by 10

Advance Organiser

We are going to multiply and divide numbers by 10

You will need: resource page A (one per child)

Whole-class work

- Write on the board: *10 × 132*.

- Explain to the children that you are going to ask them to help you find products of single-digit numbers and 132 so as to end up with the answer to 10 × 132.

- Draw a table on the board as shown.

- Complete the first row and explain the expanded notation.

- Ask how the '2 times' row can be completed. You will find some children will double, others will add.

- Invite the children to come to the board to complete each row. Repeated addition enables the rest of the 'times' rows to be completed.

- Write on the board as shown.

- Discuss what multiplying by 10 does to the digits of a number. Use the table to show how this happens to the hundreds, the tens and the units.

1×	132	▶	100	+	30	+	2	=	132
2×	132	▶		+		+		=	
3×	132	▶		+		+		=	
4×	132	▶		+		+		=	
5×	132	▶		+		+		=	
6×	132	▶		+		+		=	
7×	132	▶		+		+		=	
8×	132	▶		+		+		=	
9×	132	▶		+		+		=	
10×	132	▶		+		+		=	

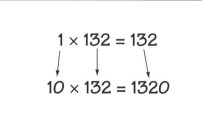

$$1 \times 132 = 132$$
$$10 \times 132 = 1320$$

- Ask the children for the division that matches the multiplication 10 × 132 = 1320.

- Write on the board: *10 × 132 = 1320 → 1320 ÷ 10 = 132.*

- Discuss this statement.

- Establish that dividing by 10 moves each digit one place to the left.

Independent, paired or group work

- Ask the children to complete resource page A.

Plenary

- Use the evidence from the examples on resource page A to write on the board the generalisations: *When a number is multiplied by 10, its digits move one place to the left. When a number is divided by 10, its digits move one place to the right.*

- Ask the children to give examples to support each statement.

Name: _____

Multiplying and dividing by 10

1 Complete the table to find 10×251.

1×	251	→	200	+	50	+	1	=	
2×		→							
3×		→							
4×		→							
5×		→							
6×		→							
7×		→							
8×		→							
9×		→							
10×		→							

2 Complete the missing numbers.

$1 \times 463 = \boxed{}$　　$1 \times 275 = \boxed{}$　　$1 \times 691 = \boxed{}$　　$1 \times 538 = \boxed{}$

$10 \times 463 = \boxed{}$　　$10 \times 275 = \boxed{}$　　$10 \times 691 = \boxed{}$　　$10 \times 538 = \boxed{}$

$760 \div 1 = \boxed{}$　　$560 \div 1 = \boxed{}$　　$240 \div 1 = \boxed{}$　　$830 \div 1 = \boxed{}$

$760 \div 10 = \boxed{}$　　$560 \div 10 = \boxed{}$　　$240 \div 10 = \boxed{}$　　$830 \div 10 = \boxed{}$

Introducing the < and the > symbols

Oral/mental starter
p 183

Advance Organiser
We are going to use symbols (signs) for more-than and less-than

Whole-class work

- Write on the board: $3 < 5$. Ask the children for suggestions as to the meaning of the < symbol.

- Explain what the < symbol or sign means.

- Invite the children to suggest ways for remembering the < symbol.

- Ask them to write on the board statements that use <.

- Write on the board a two-digit less-than statement in the following form.

- Explain that this is an inequality statement that relates 2 two-digit numbers.

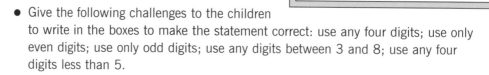

- Give the following challenges to the children to write in the boxes to make the statement correct: use any four digits; use only even digits; use only odd digits; use any digits between 3 and 8; use any four digits less than 5.

- Repeat the activity from the start with >, the *more-than* symbol or sign.

Independent, paired or group work

- Give the children pairs of numbers and ask them to write between each pair to make the statement correct.

- Give them incomplete number pairs and ask them to write in what the missing digit could be to make each statement correct.

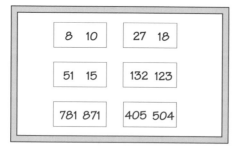

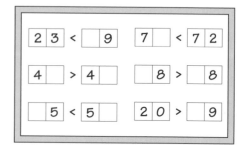

Plenary

- Ask the children to demonstrate their answers to the second part of the independent work.

- *What other digit could go here? How did you work it out?*

- Discuss both parts of the work. Ask the children to suggest one digit at a time to build up a similar statement. Discuss how they decided which digits they could choose each time.

Using the < and the > symbols

Oral/mental starter
p 183

Advance Organiser

We are going to use the symbols for more-than and less-than

You will need: a large 1 to 6 die, sets of number cards 1 to 6, 1 to 6 dice (one per pair)

Whole-class work

- Draw a three-digit inequality statement on the board and show the children the large 1 to 6 die.

- Invite a child, say James, to play this game with you.

- The objective is for Player 1 to make the inequality statement true and for Player 2 to make it false.

- James is Player 1 and you are Player 2. Player 1 goes first.

- Players take turns to roll the die and place the corresponding number card in any of the six positions in the inequality statement.

- Record each play on the board as shown.

- *Is the inequality statement correct?*

- *Who won, James or me?*

- Discuss each decision with the children. Establish what might have been a better decision and why.

Player 1		5		<			
Player 2		5		<	6		
Player 1		5		<	6		1
Player 2	3	5		<	6		1
Player 1	3	5		<	6	3	1
Player 2	3	5	2	<	6	3	1

- Ask at which roll of the dice the game was won, even though the numbers were not complete.

- Repeat the game with the > inequality statement.

☐ ☐ ☐ > ☐ ☐ ☐

Independent, paired or group work

- In pairs, the children use a 1 to 6 die to play four games.

- They then take turns to suggest digits to make up other three-digit inequality statements.

Plenary

- Work through the inequalities that some children have created and the game they played.

- End by writing a three-digit number on the board and asking children to give you a number that is more than yours and another number that is less than yours.

Properties of Number (4)

Outcome

Children will be able to extend sequences, find rules and investigate general statements

Medium-term plan objectives	• Recognise and extend number sequences formed by counting from any number in steps of a constant size, and extend beyond zero if counting back.
	• Investigate general statements about familiar numbers.
	• Explain methods and reasoning.
Overview	• Produce and extend number sequences and state their rules.
	• Test to decide if general statements are always true, sometimes true or never true.

How you could plan this unit

	Stage 1	Stage 2	Stage 3	Stage 4	Stage 5
Content and vocabulary	Extending sequences and finding the rule *count on, count back, negative number, rule*	Testing the truth of general statements *general statement, test, always true, sometimes true/never true*			
Notes	Resource page A				

Extending sequences and finding the rule

Advance Organiser

We are going to make sequences by counting on and counting back

Oral/mental starter
p 183

You will need: resource page A

Whole-class work

- Write the numbers 5 and 11 in first two boxes of a sequence.

- *This is a count-on sequence.*

- *What is the next number in the sequence?*

- Record the number in its box.

- Repeat until all nine numbers are found.

- *What is the rule for the sequence?*

- Write on the board this rule: *Start at 5, count on 6.*

- Write the numbers 35 and 27 in the first two boxes of a sequence.

- *This is a count-back sequence.*

- *What is the next number in the sequence?*

- Record the number in its box.

- Repeat until a negative number appears.

- Provide help by showing the sequence on a number line.

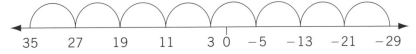

- *What is the rule for the sequence?*

- Write on the board this rule: *Start at 35, count back 8.*

Independent, paired or group work

- Ask the children to complete resource page A.

Plenary

- Go through some of the examples on resource page A.

- Remind the children that a rule for a count-on or count-back sequence should have both the start number and the count-on or count-back number.

Name: _____

Counting on and counting back

Extend each count-on or count-back sequence and complete its rule.

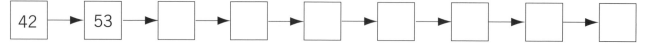

42 → 53 → ☐ → ☐ → ☐ → ☐ → ☐ → ☐ → ☐

The rule is: Start at ...., count ....

158 → 166 → ☐ → ☐ → ☐ → ☐ → ☐ → ☐ → ☐

The rule is: Start at ...., count ....

59 → 61 → ☐ → ☐ → ☐ → ☐ → ☐ → ☐ → ☐

The rule is: Start at ...., count ....

387 → 392 → ☐ → ☐ → ☐ → ☐ → ☐ → ☐ → ☐

The rule is: Start at ...., count ....

91 → 63 → ☐ → ☐ → ☐ → ☐ → ☐ → ☐ → ☐

The rule is: Start at ...., count ....

Complete these sequences.

Start at 419, count on 21

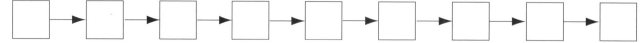
☐ → ☐ → ☐ → ☐ → ☐ → ☐ → ☐ → ☐ → ☐

Start at 48, count back 13

☐ → ☐ → ☐ → ☐ → ☐ → ☐ → ☐ → ☐ → ☐

Start at 652, count on 30

☐ → ☐ → ☐ → ☐ → ☐ → ☐ → ☐ → ☐ → ☐

Start at 507, count back 101

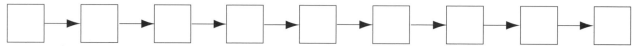
☐ → ☐ → ☐ → ☐ → ☐ → ☐ → ☐ → ☐ → ☐

Classworks © Classworks Numeracy author team, Nelson Thornes Ltd, 2003

Testing the truth of general statements

Advance Organiser

We are going to investigate general statements

Oral/mental starter
p 183

Whole-class work

- Write this general statement on the board: *Half of an even number is odd.*

- Remind the children what a general statement is.

- Explain that anyone can write a general statement, but it does not mean that it is always true. We have to provide evidence to support every general statement until we are satisfied that it is always true, sometimes true or never true.

- Build a table on the board, as shown below the general statement.

- Invite the children to give you an even number, say 14.

- Write on the board: *Half of 14 = 7 which is odd.*

Half of an even number is odd	
Numbers for which the statement is true	
Numbers for which the statement is not true	

- *Does the number 14 support the statement or not?*

- *Where shall we write 14 in the table?*

- Record 14 in the table.

- Invite the children to tell you other even numbers.

- Establish that the evidence indicates that the general statement is sometimes true, which implies it is sometimes false.

Independent, paired or group work

- In pairs, ask the children to investigate the statement *3 more than a multiple of 2 is an odd number*.

- Encourage them to investigate whether the statement is *always true, never true or sometimes true.*

Plenary

- Go through the children's findings together.

- Stress that you need many, many numbers that support a statement and none that do not support the statement to conclude that the statement is always true.

- Even then, somewhere there may be a number that does not support the statement, but as yet we have not found it.

Properties of Number (5)

Outcome

Children will be able to multiply by 100 and order four-digit numbers

Medium-term plan objectives	• Begin to multiply whole numbers by 100. • Order a set of whole numbers up to 10,000. • Round any positive integer to the nearest 10 or 100. • Read a variety of scales and dials to a suitable degree of accuracy.
Overview	• Multiply whole numbers up to 1000 by 100. • Put numbers up to 1000 in order.

How you could plan this unit

	Stage 1	Stage 2	Stage 3	Stage 4	Stage 5
Content and vocabulary	Multiplying whole numbers by 100 *multiplying by 100, general statement, missing numbers*	Ordering four-digit numbers *order, smallest, largest*			
Notes	Resource page A				

20

Multiplying whole numbers by 100

Advance Organiser

We are going to multiply numbers by 100

Oral/mental starter
p 183

You will need: resource page A (one per child)

Whole-class work

- Write on the board the first row of the diagram.

- *What is the answer to 38 × 1?*

- Record 38.

- Write the second row below.

- *What is 38 × 10?*

- Record 380.

- Discuss how to find 38 × 10 × 10 using the answer to 38 × 10.

- Invite the children to explain what happens to the digits as 38 is multiplied by 10 and then by 10 again.

- Repeat the activity for 61.

- *What is 10 × 10?*

- Explain that we can replace the 10 × 10 in the last row by 100, as multiplying by 10 and then 10 again is the same as multiplying by 100.

- *What happens to the digits of a number when it is multiplied by 100?*

- Write on the board this general statement: *When a number is multiplied by 100 its digits move two places to the left. Zeros are written in the empty places.*

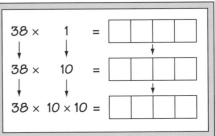

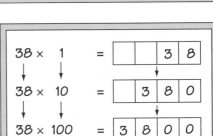

Independent, paired or group work

- Ask the children to complete resource page A.

Plenary

- Go through the examples on resource page A.

- Ask the children to describe what happens to the digits of a number when it is multiplied by 10 and by 100.

(**PUPIL PAGE**)

Name: _____

Multiplying by 100

1 Complete the missing digits.

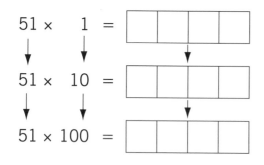

51 ×   1 =
51 × 10 =
51 × 100 =

14 ×   1 =
14 × 10 =
14 × 100 =

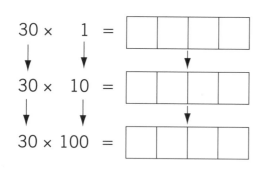

30 ×   1 =
30 × 10 =
30 × 100 =

89 ×   1 =
89 × 10 =
89 × 100 =

2 Find the answers.

26 × 1 =

26 × 10 =

26 × 100 =

55 × 1 =

55 × 10 =

55 × 100 =

3 Write in the missing numbers.

214 × 10 =

357 × 100 =

⬚ × 10 = 4930

⬚ × 100 = 67200

28 × ⬚ = 2800

419 × ⬚ = 4190

Ordering four-digit numbers

Oral/mental starter p 183

Advance Organiser

We are going to put numbers in order

Whole-class work

- Write on the board the four incomplete numbers as shown.

| 3 | 7 | | | | 3 | 7 | | | | 3 | 7 | | | | 3 | 7 | | |

- Ask the children for any two digits to complete each number in turn.

| 3 | 7 | 2 | 5 | | 3 | 7 | 6 | 4 | | 3 | 7 | 1 | 9 | | 3 | 7 | 4 | 7 |

- *Which is the smallest of the four numbers?*

- *How did you decide?*

- Establish that the order for comparing is thousands, hundreds, tens and finally units. Record: *3719*.

- Repeat for the remaining numbers in turn.

- *By repeatedly finding the smallest number we have put the four numbers in order, smallest first.*

| 3 | 7 | 1 | 9 | | 3 | 7 | 2 | 5 | | 3 | 7 | 4 | 7 | | 3 | 7 | 6 | 4 |

Independent, paired or group work

- Ask the children to use the digits 4, 7 and 8 to make four different four-digit numbers. They will need to use the digits more than once for each number. Ask them to write the four numbers in order, smallest first, using similar boxes to the ones above.

- Ask them to repeat the exercise using only the digits 9 and 5. They write them in order, largest first.

- Write the following incomplete numbers on the board and tell the children they are in order, smallest first.

- *Write in what the missing digits could be.*

| | 4 | 2 | | 3 | | 9 | | 3 | | 9 | | | 4 | 9 |

Plenary

- Discuss the different solutions for the final question.

- Remind the children of the method for comparing numbers to put them in order (beginning with the digit on the left, that is, with the greatest place value).

Properties of Number (6)

Outcome

Children will be able to investigate multiples and use their knowledge to solve puzzles

Medium-term plan objectives

- Recognise multiples of 2, 3, 4, 5, 10, up to the tenth multiple.
- Solve number problems and puzzles.
- Explain methods and reasoning, orally and in writing.

Overview

- Recognise and use multiples of 2, 3, 4, 5 and 10.
- Solve a puzzle using threes and any of the four operations.

How you could plan this unit

	Stage 1	Stage 2	Stage 3	Stage 4	Stage 5
Content and vocabulary	Finding and using multiples *multiple, times-table*	Solving a puzzle using threes *add, subtract, multiply, divide*			
Notes	Resource page A				

Finding and using multiples

Advance Organiser

We are going to work with multiples of numbers

You will need: resource page A (one per child)

Whole-class work

- Draw a blank grid on the board as shown.

Multiples of 2	0	2	4	6	8	10	12	14	16	18	20
Multiples of 3											
Multiples of 4											
Multiples of 5											
Multiples of 10											

- Together, count on in twos starting at 0.
- *What do you notice about the numbers in the count-on-in-twos sequence?*
- *The numbers in the count-on-in-twos sequence, starting with 0, are multiples of 2. Why is this?*
- Remind the children that multiples of 2 are numbers that are in the 2 times-table.
- Record the numbers in the first row of the grid.
- *What is special about multiples of 2?*
- Repeat the activity for count-on-in-threes, -fours, -fives and -tens. Remove the grid from the board and tell the children they are going to answer some questions by making their own grid.

Independent, paired or group work

- Ask the children to complete the table on resource page A.

Plenary

- Work through resource page A with the children and ask questions about the table.
- *Sixteen is a multiple of which numbers?*
- *List the numbers that are a multiple of both 2 and 3.*
- *Write the number that is a multiple of both 4 and 5.*
- *Find the number that is a multiple of 2, 4, 5 and 10.*
- *Which multiple of 4 has the sum of its digits as 6?*
- *Which two multiples of 3 have digits that have a difference of 1?*
- *Find a multiple of 2 that is double a multiple of 3.*
- *Find a multiple of 5 that is half a multiple of 4.*
- Discuss their answers to the questions – what did they notice?
- Ask the children to suggest reasons for what they found.

Name: _____

Finding multiples of numbers

Complete the multiples of 2, 3, 4, 5 and 10 starting with 0 each time.

Multiples of 2											
Multiples of 3											
Multiples of 4											
Multiples of 5											
Multiples of 10											

Solving a puzzle using threes

Advance Organiser

We are going to use threes to make other numbers

Whole-class work

- Draw a table on the board as shown, leaving out the equations initially.

- Tell the children that the number 1 can be made using 2 lots of 3 and the operation of division.

- Ask them to suggest how to do it.

- Work through some ideas and, if necessary, point out that they can make the answer 1 by performing $3 \div 3 = 1$.

- Record the calculation in the column on the right.

- Ask the children to find out how to make number 4 using only threes and any of the operations $+$, $-$, $\times$ and $\div$.

- Record any successful ways in the table. Some examples are given.

Number	How to make it using threes
1	$3 \div 3 = 1$
2	
3	
4	$3 + (3 \div 3) = 4$
5	
6	
7	
8	$(3 \times 3) - (3 \div 3) = 8$
9	
10	
11	
12	$(3 \times 3) + 3 = 12$
13	
14	
15	
16	
17	
18	$(3 + 3) \times 3 = 18$
19	
20	

Independent, paired or group work

- Children work in pairs, investigating ways of making the numbers 1 to 20 using only threes and any of the operations $+$, $-$, $\times$ and $\div$, recording their attempts on a similar table.

Plenary

- Collect on the table the children's attempts for each of the numbers 1 to 20.

- Discuss different methods.

Addition and Subtraction (1)

Outcome

Children will be able to use a variety of informal paper and pencil methods to add and subtract

Medium-term plan objectives

- Consolidate the understanding of the relationship between addition and subtraction.
- Understand the principles (not names) of commutative law for addition.
- Count on or count back in repeated steps of 1, 10 or 100.
- Identify near-doubles.
- Count up through next multiple of 10, 100 or 1000.
- Use informal pencil and paper methods to support, record or explain addition and subtraction.

Overview

- Make two additions and two subtractions given three numbers.
- Use near-doubles to add.
- Subtract by counting up through a multiple of 10, 100 or 1000.
- Add two three-digit numbers using an informal method.

How you could plan this unit

	Stage 1	Stage 2	Stage 3	Stage 4	Stage 5
Content and vocabulary	Relating addition and subtraction *addition, subtraction, relationship*	Addition of near-doubles *round numbers, near doubles*	Subtracting by counting up *nearest multiple of 10, 100, 1000, counting up, unmarked number line*	Informal addition *place value, informal method*	
Notes					

Relating addition and subtraction

Advance Organiser

We are going to use the same numbers to make additions and subtractions

Oral/mental starter
p 184

You will need: five sets of number cards 12, 15, 27

Whole-class work

- Draw the diagram (empty) on the board, as shown. Put the number cards 12, 15 and 27 in the centre boxes.

- Explain that the arrows from the circle indicate that the three numbers are to be used to make two additions and two subtractions.

- *Tell me an addition that can be made using the three numbers in the centre.* (Say $15 + 12 = 27$.)

- Use number cards to complete the addition in the top left.

- *What is the subtraction that is related to this addition?*

- Use number cards to complete $27 - 12 = 15$ in the bottom left.

- Explain that 12 was added to 15 to make 27, so 12 is subtracted from 27 to make 15. Subtraction undoes addition.

- *What does the arrow from the addition to the subtraction tell you?*

- Repeat the activity for the other addition and subtraction.

- Explain the meaning of the arrows joining the two additions and the two subtractions.

- Tell the children that the whole diagram shows how addition and subtraction are related for any three numbers.

Diagram showing: top left $15 + 12 = 27$ and top right $12 + 15 = 27$; centre circle containing 15, 12, 27; bottom left $27 - 12 = 15$ and bottom right $27 - 15 = 12$, with arrows connecting them.

Independent, paired or group work

- Ask the children to make similar diagrams for sets of three numbers such as: 15, 6 and 9; 35, 55 and 90; 300, 200 and 500; 69, 26 and 43.

- They can then choose three more numbers that will make an addition, and write a similar diagram for those.

Plenary

- Work through the diagrams with the children. Continually stress the relationships between the additions, the subtractions, and the additions and the subtractions.

- Remind the children that once they have an addition, they can make another addition and two subtractions using the same numbers.

Addition of near-doubles

Oral/mental starter
p 184

Advance Organiser

We are going to find easy ways of adding

Whole-class work

- Write on the board: *31 + 32*.

- *What is the answer to 31 add 32?*

- Discuss the different methods that the children used.

- Explain that sometimes it is easier to work with 'round' numbers'. These are usually multiples of 10, and sometimes multiples of 5.

- *What is a 'round' number that is very near 31 and 32?*

- Build up on the board the 'near doubles' diagram as shown, explaining at each stage what you are doing and asking why it works.

- Emphasise the importance of choosing easier doubles to work with. Children must also realise that 60 + 3 has the same answer as 31 + 32.

- Explain how the diagram can be simplified using only symbols.

- At each stage, ask the children to explain what you are doing and why it works.

- Relate the workings to the diagram, where appropriate.

- Stress that each line is another way of writing the same addition that has the same answer. That is the reason for an = sign at the start of each line.

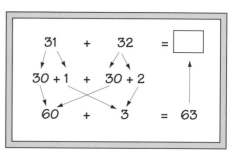

$$31 + 32$$
$$= 30 + 1 + 30 + 2$$
$$= 30 + 30 + 1 + 2$$
$$= 60 + 3$$
$$= 63$$

Independent, paired or group work

- Ask the children to solve similar additions using either or both methods; for example, 43 + 42, 54 + 57, 79 + 77, 63 + 58. Some children may need help with the near-doubles that involve subtracting.

- Extend to 148 + 147 and 302 + 296 and so on.

$$79 + 77$$
$$= 80 - 1 + 80 - 3$$
$$= 80 + 80 - 1 - 3$$
$$= 160 - 4$$
$$= 156$$

Plenary

- Work through some of the children's answers. Check that the children have written the additions in a systematic way with the = signs below each other. Make sure they understand how important this is.

Subtracting by counting up

Advance Organiser

We are going to work out subtractions using a number line

Oral/mental starter p 184

Whole-class work

- Write on the board: *83 − 78*.

- *What is the answer to 83 subtract 78?*

- Discuss the different methods the children have used.

- Show them how an unmarked number line can help.

- Point out that although the calculation is a subtraction, the answer can be worked out by counting up from the smaller number to the larger number.

- *What we are doing is finding the difference.*

- Describe the procedure, step-by-step, asking what is being done and why.

- *Step 1*: Mark 78 and 83 somewhere on the number line with 78 on the left and 83 on the right as they would appear on a marked number line.

- *Step 2*: Choose the nearest multiple of 10 that is more than 78 (80). Mark this on the number line. Ensure that the children understand that 80 is between 78 and 83.

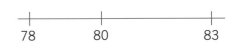

- *Step 3*: Count how many from 78 to 80. Show this as a jump of 2.

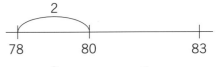

- *Step 4*: Count on from 80 to 83. Show this as a jump of 3.

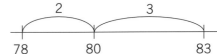

- *Step 5*: Count up the total of the two jumps, that is *2 + 3 = 5*.

- *Step 6*: Write *83 − 78 = 5*.

- Repeat for *302 − 289*. Here the steps involve a multiple of 10 and of 100.

Independent, paired or group work

- Ask the children to use similar methods to solve 75 − 67, 204 − 196, 502 − 488, 3003 − 2995.

- Children can use jottings or other methods if they prefer for further questions; for example, 52 − 46, 91 − 87, 407 − 389, 705 − 692, 6004 − 5986.

Plenary

- Select examples of the children's work to go through together.

- Ask what kind of jottings children used for the later questions.

Informal addition

Advance Organiser

We are going to use an informal way of adding

Oral/mental starter p 184

Whole-class work

- Write on the board: *658 + 237*.
- *What is the answer to 658 add 237?*
- Discuss the different methods the children have used.
- Explain that you are going to show them a method that writes the numbers below each other to keep units, tens and hundreds in place.
- You may find it helpful to use squared paper or squares on the board.
- Describe the procedure, step-by-step, asking what is being done and why.
- Involve the children at every stage.
- *Step 1*: Write 658 + 237 vertically so that the units, tens and hundreds, are in columns.
- *Step 2*: Break down the addition into an addition of the hundreds, the tens and the units. Recording each is important at this informal stage, as are the = signs.
- *Step 3*: Calculate each addition, keeping the digits in the correct place value columns.
- *Step 4*: Find the sum of the three additions.

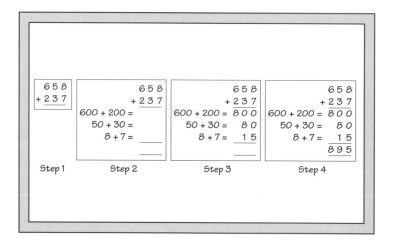

- Repeat the activity for 482 + 365.

Independent, paired or group work

- Ask the children to set out and solve similar additions, such as 716 + 159, 637 + 254, 272 + 685, 167 + 248 and so on.
- They can then make up additions involving three-digit numbers for each other to solve.

Plenary

- Invite the children to describe and explain how they worked out the answers.
- Emphasise the point made in the steps in the whole-class work.
- Ask the children to read out the additions they made up and discuss how to solve them.

Addition and Subtraction (2)

Outcome

Children will be able to use more formal methods of written addition and subtraction

Medium-term plan objectives

- Consolidate understanding of subtraction as the inverse of addition.
- Find a small difference by counting up.
- Use the relationship between addition and subtraction.
- Develop written methods for addition and subtraction of whole numbers less than 1000.

Overview

- Use addition and subtraction as inverse operations.
- Use a more formal method to add two three-digit numbers.
- Use a decomposition method with expanded notation to subtract.

How you could plan this unit

	Stage 1	Stage 2	Stage 3	Stage 4	Stage 5
Content and vocabulary	Subtraction as the inverse of addition *subtraction, inverse operation*	A more formal method of addition *vertical addition*	A more formal method of subtraction *vertical subtraction, expanded notation*		
Notes					

Subtraction as the inverse of addition

Advance Organiser

We are going to investigate the relationship between addition and subtraction

Oral/mental starter p 184

Whole-class work

- Draw an 'inverse' diagram on the board, as shown.

- Explain the diagram, and that there are three missing numbers: one for adding, one for subtracting and a middle number that is the result of adding.

- Ask the children to work in pairs to find the three missing numbers in the boxes.

- Collect different answers, asking the children how they found the missing numbers.

- Discuss why the start and end numbers are the same.

- Write on the board the general statement: *Adding any number to a start number and subtracting the same number from the sum gives an answer that is the same as the start number.*

- Ask the children to give examples of the general statement.

- Remind them that subtraction is the inverse of addition – it undoes what addition did to a number.

- Repeat the activity with this inverse diagram.

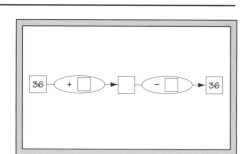

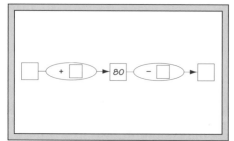

Independent, paired or group work

- Ask the children to work with similar diagrams, or another method if they prefer, to solve other problems. Try some of the examples as shown.

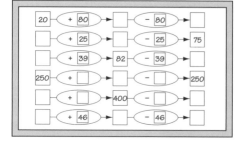

Plenary

- Invite the children to explain how they completed the examples, shown above.

- Stress that 'addition undoes subtraction' and 'subtraction undoes addition' as they are inverse operations.

A more formal method of addition

Oral/mental starter
p 184

Advance Organiser

We are going to add two three-digit numbers

Whole-class work

- Write this addition on the board vertically: 658 + 237.

- Question the children about the informal method they have been using (as below).

- Complete the addition using the informal method.

- Explain that some of what is written can be worked out mentally and need not be written down.

- *Which parts of the method do you think we need not write down as we can do it in our heads?*

- Develop the addition again without writing the separate additions.

- It is important that each part addition is said taking into account its place value; for example, as 600 + 200, rather than as 6 + 2. This emphasises the true value of each digit.

	658	658
	+237	+237
600 + 200 =	800	800
50 + 30 =	80 →	80
8 + 7 =	15	15
	895	895

- Repeat the activity with 387 + 256 and 619 + 342.

Independent, paired or group work

- Ask the children to complete, using either method or a combination of both, additions such as 658 + 247, 475 + 183, 447 + 392, 488 + 463, 277 + 550 and 292 + 608.

- Then ask them to make up and solve three of their own three-digit additions.

Plenary

- Invite the children to explain how they worked out the examples above.

- Write on the board as the children describe their method.

- Discuss any differences with the children.

A *more formal method of subtraction*

Advance Organiser

We are going to use a new method for subtraction

Oral/mental starter
p 184

Whole-class work

- Write this subtraction on the board vertically: *643 − 18*.

- Develop the decomposition method using the expanded notation step-by-step.

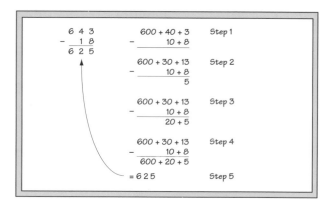

- As you proceed, ask the children what you are doing and why.

- *Step 1*: Expand each number into hundreds, tens and units. Make sure that they are kept underneath each other.

- *Step 2*: Subtract the units first. *We start with the units. We need a 10 as there may not be enough units to do the subtraction.* Say '*3 subtract 8*', as this keeps the order of *top subtract bottom*. The response should be: *There are not enough to do the subtraction as 3 is less than 8. We should not say '3 subtract 8 we cannot do', as we can, it is −5. We use one of the tens. (WE DO NOT BORROW.) This changes the number of tens to 3 and makes the number of units into 13. The subtraction of the units is now 13 subtract 8.* Record the 5 in the units answer position.

- *Step 3*: Now subtract the tens. *30 subtract 10 is 20.* Record the 20 in the tens answer position.

- *Step 4*: Now subtract the hundreds. *As there are no hundreds to subtract (we could say that there are zero hundreds to subtract) we record 600 in the hundreds answer position.*

- *Step 5*: Add the hundreds, tens and units to give 625. Transfer the answer to the answer box in the vertical subtraction.

- Repeat with 725 − 87. Note the steps are slightly different as more tens are needed, as well as units.

Independent, paired or group work

- Ask the children to solve similar subtractions in a similar way; for example, 484 − 57, 825 − 72, 326 − 68 and so on.

Plenary

- Work through a selection of the questions with the children.

- Write up a method as the children describe it. Ask different children to take up the description at a different stage.

Addition and Subtraction (3)

Outcome

Children will be able to use more specific mental and written methods, as appropriate, to add

---

Medium-term plan objectives

- Understand the principle (not name) of commutative law for addition, not subtraction.
- Add several numbers by finding pairs that total 10, 9 or 11.
- Partition into tens and units, adding tens first.
- Add three two-digit multiples of 10.
- Develop and refine written methods for addition and subtraction, including money.

Overview

- Add several small numbers by making tens.
- Add by partitioning into tens and ones.
- Add multiples of 10.
- Add money using a standard written method.

How you could plan this unit

	Stage 1	Stage 2	Stage 3	Stage 4	Stage 5
Content and vocabulary	Add several numbers by making tens *pairs of numbers that make 10*	Adding by partitioning *partitioning, tens, ones*	Addition of three multiples of 10 *multiples of 10*	Addition of money using a standard method *money, total cost, decimal point, carrying*	
Notes					

Add several numbers by making tens

Oral/mental starter
p 184

Advance Organiser

We are going to look for pairs that make 10 when adding

Whole-class work

- Write on the board: $7 + 3 + 8 + 2 + 5 =$ and $3 + 5 + 8 + 7 + 2 =$.

- *Find the answer to each addition in your heads.*

- Discuss the different methods the children used.

- *Why do the two additions have the same answer?*

- *Which addition was easier to do? Why?*

- Explain that pairing numbers that make 10 makes additions easier to do.

- Build on the board the diagram for $7 + 3 + 8 + 2 + 5$, as shown.

- Explain that, sometimes, pairs of numbers that make 10 are not next to each other, but you can join them as if they were, to make the addition easier.

- Build on the board the diagram for $3 + 5 + 8 + 7 + 2$, as shown.

- Write on the board these additions: $1 + 12 + 4 + 9 + 6$, $5 + 14 + 7 + 5 + 3$ and $8 + 4 + 7 + 2 + 6$.

- *Find pairs that make 10 in each addition. What are the answers?*

- Invite the children to join up each pair that makes 10.

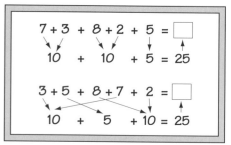

Independent, paired or group work

- Ask the children to solve similar additions, joining pairs that make 10 each time; for example, $3 + 7 + 21$, $9 + 16 + 1$, $8 + 6 + 2 + 4$, $5 + 5 + 7 + 3$, $4 + 13 + 2 + 6 + 8$, $1 + 3 + 22 + 9 + 7$ and so on.

Plenary

- Ask the children to explain how they found the answers.

- Check that they looked for pairs that made 10, and whether they counted up in tens to find the answers.

- Ask the children if anyone used any other methods for any of the questions.

- Draw the following diagram on the board and ask the children to help you solve it.

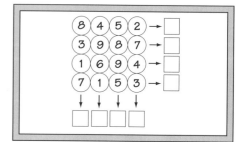

Adding by partitioning

Advance Organiser

We are going to split numbers into tens and units so that we can add them

Oral/mental starter p 184

Whole-class work

- Write this addition on the board: *56 + 27*.

- *Work out 56 + 27 in your heads. What is the answer?*

- Discuss the different methods that the children have used.

- Explain that one method is to split, or partition, the numbers into tens and ones.

- Build the diagram, as shown on the board, step-by-step, making sure that the children understand what is happening.

- Explain that diagrams can be helpful, but they take lots of time to work out.

- Show the children how to write the addition using symbols. Put the symbolic working at the side of the diagram.

- Build each line in turn making sure the children understand what is happening and why. Refer to the diagram so that the children realise that the processes are the same in symbols as they are in the diagram.

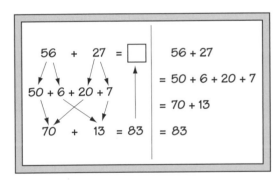

- Remind them that the = sign at the start of each line tells them that the addition on each line has the same answer as 56 + 27.

- Stress that the = signs should be in a line below each other, to make the working systematic.

- Repeat the activity for 39 + 45.

Independent, paired or group work

- Ask the children to complete similar additions, using either or both methods.

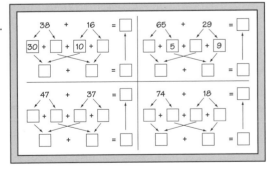

Plenary

- Invite the children to explain how they worked out some of the above questions.

- Work through some other examples, such as 29 + 45, 36 + 57, 48 + 39 and 55 + 28.

Addition of three multiples of 10

Oral/mental starter
p 184

Advance Organiser

We are going to add multiples of 10

Whole-class work

- Write this addition on the board: *30 + 40 + 80*.

- *What is the answer to 30 + 40 + 80?*

- Discuss the different methods the children have used.

- Explain that adding multiples of 10 is like adding single digits.

- Build the three additions on the board.

- *In what ways are the three additions alike?*

- *In what ways are the three additions different?*

- Discuss how finding the answer to 3 + 4 + 8 helps to find the answer to the other two additions.

- Repeat the activity with these three additions.

> 3 + 4 + 8 =
>
> 3 tens + 4 tens + 8 tens =
>
> 30 + 40 + 80 =

> 7 + 2 + 6 =
>
> 7 tens + 2 tens + 6 tens =
>
> 70 + 20 + 60 =

Independent, paired or group work

- Ask the children to complete the following.

  5 + 9 + 3 = ☐   4 + 1 + 8 = ☐
  5 tens + 9 tens + 3 tens = ☐   4 tens + 1 ten + 8 tens = ☐
  50 + 90 + 30 = ☐   40 + 10 + 80 = ☐

- They should then use any method to solve calculations such as 60 + 50 + 90, 20 + 80 + 60, 70 + 90 + 80, 80 + 60 + 70 and so on.

Plenary

- Invite the children to explain how they found the answers to the above questions.

- Draw a diagram on the board as shown and ask the children to help you solve each part. They have to find the total of each row and column.

- End by reading out some additions of three multiples of 10.

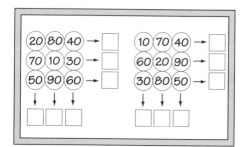

Addition of money using a standard method

Oral/mental starter
p 184

Advance Organiser

We are going to find the total cost of two items

Whole-class work

- Write this problem on the board: *A torch costs £3.85 and a battery costs £2.47. What is the total cost of the two items?*

- Ask the children to work out the total cost.

- Discuss the different methods of adding that the children have used.

- Build the addition on the board, step-by-step. Make sure the children understand what you are doing and why. Stress the importance of keeping the decimal points that separates the pounds from the pence, lined up under each other.

- Introduce 'carrying' below the line relating each step to the previous method.

- Repeat the activity with £5.46 and £4.28.

```
    £ 3 . 8 5
  + £ 2 . 4 7
        . 1 2
      1 . 2 0
      5 . 0 0
    £ 6 . 3 2
```

```
    £ 3 . 8 5        £ 3 . 8 5
  + £ 2 . 4 7      + £ 2 . 4 7
        . 1 2        £ 6 . 3 2
      1 . 2 0           1    1
      5 . 0 0
    £ 6 . 3 2
```

Independent, paired or group work

- Ask the children to solve £2.48 + £4.69 and £1.32 + £7.95 using a similar method.

- Ask them to make up more additions of money for each other to solve. Encourage them to record their working each time.

Plenary

- Work through the examples that the children have completed.

- Stress how important it is to write the decimal points under each other.

- Discuss any differences in method or answer.

Addition and Subtraction (4)

Outcome

Children will be able to choose appropriate mental methods to solve additions and subtractions

Medium-term plan objectives	• Understand the principles (not names) of associative law for addition.
	• Add or subtract the nearest multiple of 10 and adjust.
	• Use number facts and place value to add or subtract mentally any pair of two-digit whole numbers.
	• Develop and refine written methods for column addition and subtraction.
Overview	• Recognise the use of the associative law.
	• Add 9, 19, 29 and so on to a two-digit number.
	• Subtract 9, 19, 29 and so on from a two-digit number.
	• Subtract two-digit numbers using different methods.

How you could plan this unit

	Stage 1	Stage 2	Stage 3	Stage 4	Stage 5
Content and vocabulary	Investigating the associative law of addition *brackets*	Adding the nearest multiple of 10 and adjusting *add, multiple of 10, adjust*	Subtracting the nearest multiple of 10 and adjusting *subtract*	Subtracting two-digit numbers *different methods, decide, choose*	
Notes					

Investigating the associative law of addition

Advance Organiser

We are going to compare additions when using brackets

Whole-class work

- Write these additions on the board: *(7 + 4) + 3 and 7 + (4 + 3)*.
- Explain the purpose of the brackets.
- *Work out the answer of each addition.*
- Discuss the methods the children have used.
- Show them that the additions in the brackets should be calculated first.
- *Why are the answers the same?*
- Write on the board the open additions as shown.
- Explain that the numbers in the shapes are the same when the shape is the same.
- Show how this works for the example above with 7, 4 and 3.
- Remind them that with these numbers the two additions have the same answer, but it may be because there is something special about these three numbers.

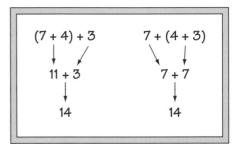

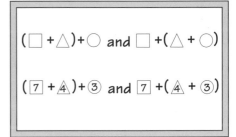

- Tell the children that you are going to take a vote. They each have to decide:
  1) will the two additions always have the same answer whatever the numbers used; or
  2) will there be some numbers that make the two additions have different answers?
- Write each option on the board.
- Give them time to think and then take a vote – say the two options in turn and ask for a show of hands. Put the voting on the board.
- Explain to them that you will tell them later who is correct and why.

Independent, paired or group work

- Draw a table on the board, as shown, and explain how to complete the first row of the table.
- Ask the children to copy and complete it in their books.

□	△	○	(□+△)+○	□+(△+○)	Are the answers the same?
8	6	9			
5	12	7			
9	4	11			
20	70	50			
33	22	44			
75	25	44			
26	37	15			
400	200	600			

Plenary

- Put the two options to the children. Ask them to vote again.
- Discuss why the two additions are always the same whatever the numbers are.
- Warn them that although it works for addition it does not work for subtraction.
- Show them that (9 − 5) − 2 is not equal to 9 − (5 − 2).

Adding the nearest multiple of 10 and adjusting

Advance Organiser

We are going to add numbers such as 19, 29, 39 and 49

Whole-class work

- Write this addition on the board: *54 + 39.*

- *What is the answer to 54 + 39?*

- Discuss the different methods the children have used.

- Build the diagram as shown, step-by-step, explaining what you are doing and why.

- Make sure the children understand the purpose of the arrows.

- Establish that the calculations in each of the three rows have the same answer.

- Explain that the diagram is helpful to understand what is happening, but it is simpler to use symbols.

- Build the calculations with symbols, preferably at the side of the diagram. Relate the symbolic method to the diagram where appropriate.

- Repeat the activity with the addition 46 + 29.

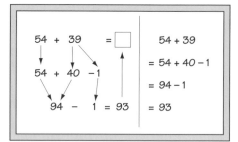

Independent, paired or group work

- Ask the children to use either or both methods to solve the following calculations: 62 + 19, 27 + 49, 58 + 29, 36 + 59 and so on.

- Ask them to build the answers to the calculations as shown on the right.

- Ask the children to apply similar methods to find the answers to 53 + 29 and 68 + 39.

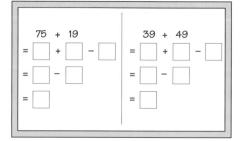

Plenary

- Invite the children to explain how they worked out the answers to various questions.

- Discuss any differences in method or answer.

- Work through some more additions if necessary.

Subtracting the nearest multiple of 10 and adjusting

Oral/mental starter
p 184

Advance Organiser

We are going to subtract numbers such as 19, 29, 39 and 49

Whole-class work

- Write this subtraction on the board: $47 - 19$.

- *Work out the answer to $47 - 19$.*

- Discuss the different methods the children have used.

- Build the diagram as shown, step-by-step, explaining what you are doing and why.

- Make sure the children understand the purpose of the arrows.

- Establish that the calculations in each of the three rows have the same answer.

- Explain that the diagram is helpful to understand what is happening, but it is simpler to use symbols.

- Build the calculations with symbols, preferably at the side of the diagram. Relate the symbolic method to the diagram where appropriate.

- Repeat the activity with the subtraction $63 - 29$.

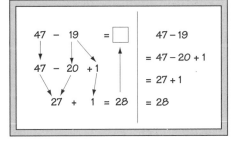

Independent, paired or group work

- Ask the children to answer the following questions using either or both of the above methods: $58 - 39$, $84 - 59$, $76 - 49$ and $32 - 19$.

- Ask them to build and solve the subtractions on the right.

- Then ask the children to apply an appropriate method to find answers to $83 - 29$ and $72 - 59$.

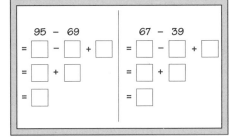

Plenary

- Invite the children to explain how they worked out the answers to some of the above questions.

- Work through their answers, asking for different methods and ideas each time.

Subtracting two-digit numbers

**Oral/mental starter
p 184**

Advance Organiser

We are going to use different methods to subtract

Whole-class work

- Write this subtraction on the board: $54 - 28$.

- *Work out the answer to $54 - 28$.*

- Invite the children to explain the method they used.

- Some possibilities are shown below.

$54 - 28$	$54 - 28$	$54 - 28$	$54 - 28$	$54 - 28$
$= 54 - 30 + 2$	$= 58 - 4 - 28$	$= 54 - 20 - 8$	$= 50 + 4 - 20 - 8$	$= 56 - 30$
$= 24 + 2$	$= 30 - 4$	$= 34 - 8$	$= 30 - 4$	$= 26$
$= 26$	$= 26$	$= 26$	$= 26$	

- Write each child's method on the board in a systematic way.

- Write this subtraction on the board: $73 - 35$.

- Ask the children to find the answer to $73 - 35$ using one of the methods shown on the board. Write other two-digit subtractions on the board and again ask children to choose and work through one of the methods.

- Encourage them to use different methods for different types of subtraction – thinking about what would make each one easier to solve each time.

Independent, paired or group work

- Ask the children to find six different ways to complete a two-digit subtraction so that the answer is always 24. Give them one digit to start with.

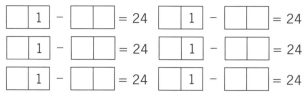

- Ask them to repeat with the following subtractions, this time ensuring the answer is always 37.

Plenary

- Choose one of the questions that the children have written. Ask them to explain their method of finding the answer to each one.

- Make a list of each method and discuss how some children have suggested different methods to other children, and that some questions might be solved more easily using one method than another.

Addition and Subtraction (5)

Outcome

Children will be able to work systematically to solve a problem, using their knowledge of addition and subtraction

Medium-term plan objectives	• Consolidate understanding of relationship between addition and subtraction.
	• Add and subtract, mentally, any pair of two-digit whole numbers.
	• Refine written methods for column addition and subtraction.
Overview	• Add and subtract, mentally, two-digit numbers.
	• Add and subtract three-digit numbers using a written column method.

How you could plan this unit

	Stage 1	Stage 2	Stage 3	Stage 4	Stage 5
Content and vocabulary	Finding the largest/ smallest sum and difference for two-digit numbers *largest/smallest sum, largest/smallest difference, two-digit number*	Finding the largest/ smallest sum and difference for three-digit numbers *three-digit number*			
Notes					

47

Finding the largest/smallest sum and difference for two-digit numbers

Advance Organiser

We are going to investigate two-digit numbers

Whole-class work

- Draw on the board five blank two-digit numbers as shown.

- *How many missing digits are there in the five numbers?*

- Write the digits 0 to 9 on the board.

- *How many digits have I written on the board?*

  □□ □□ □□ □□ □□

  0 1 2 3 4 5 6 7 8 9

- Invite the children, in turn, to write a digit in a box to create a set of two-digit numbers.

- Note: the 0 digit should not be placed in a tens box. If this occurs, discuss why this does not make a two-digit number.

- As each digit is used, cross it off the list.

- Ask the children to mentally find the pair of two-digit numbers that make the largest sum.

  |3|6| |1|4| |5|9| |7|2| |8|0|

  0̸ 1̸ 2̸ 3̸ 4̸ 5̸ 6̸ 7̸ 8̸ 9̸

  |7|2| + |8|0| = 152

- Record suggestions from the children and discuss them.

- *How did you decide which pair has the largest sum?*

- Discuss the strategy of choosing the pair that has the largest two tens.

- Ask the children to mentally find the pair of two-digit numbers that makes the smallest sum.

- Record suggestions from the children in a table and discuss them.

- *How did you decide which pair has the smallest sum?*

- Discuss the strategy of choosing the pair that have the smallest (least number of) tens.

  |3|6| + |1|4| = 50

Independent, paired or group work

- Explain the following investigation. Children work in pairs to use each of these digits only once to make five two-digit numbers.

  0 1 2 3 4 5 6 7 8 9

  □□ □□ □□ □□ □□

- They investigate which pair of numbers has the largest difference and which pair has the smallest difference. Encourage them to record their work.

Plenary

- Compare the results from each pair from the investigation.

- Discuss a variety of subtractions and findings.

Finding the largest/smallest sum and difference for three-digit numbers

Advance Organiser

We are going to investigate three-digit numbers

Oral/mental starter p 184

Whole-class work

- Draw on the board three blank three-digit numbers.
- *How many missing digits are there in the three numbers?*
- Write the digits 1 to 9 on the board.
- *How many digits have I written on the board?*
- Invite the children, in turn, to write a digit in a box to make three lots of three-digit numbers.
- As each digit is used, cross it off the list.
- Ask the children to use a written column method to find the pair of three-digit numbers that make the largest sum.
- Record suggestions from the children and discuss them.
- Work the addition on the board to consolidate the method.
- *How did you decide which pair has the largest sum?*
- Discuss the strategy of choosing the pair that has the largest two tens.
- Ask the children to use a written column method to find the pair of three-digit numbers that make the smallest sum.
- Record suggestions from the children in a table and discuss them.
- Work the addition on the board to consolidate the method.
- *How did you decide which pair has the smallest sum?*
- Discuss the strategy of choosing the pair that have the smallest tens total.

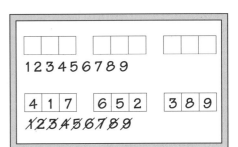

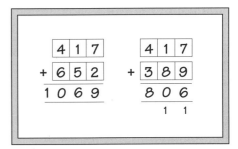

Independent, paired or group work

- Introduce the following investigation and ask children to work in pairs.
- *Use each of the digits 1 to 9 only once to make three lots of three-digit numbers.*
- *Investigate the three possible differences of pairs of your numbers.*
- *What is the largest difference? What is the smallest difference?*
- *Repeat the investigation, but try to make three-digit numbers so that the largest difference is larger than the one you have just made.*

Plenary

- Compare the results from each pair from the investigation.

Multiplication and Division (1)

Outcome

Children will be able to understand relationships between operations and calculations, and support their mental work using jottings

Medium-term plan objectives

- Extend understanding of × and ÷ and their relationship to each other and to + and −.

- Use doubling and halving of two-digit numbers; for example, multiply by 4 = double then double, multiply by 5 = multiply by 10 then halve, multiply by 20 = multiply by 10 then double, 8 times-table = 4 times-table then double, quarters = half of one-half.

- Approximating first, use informal pencil and paper methods to multiply and divide.

Overview

- Relate multiplication and division to addition and subtraction.

- Use knowledge of doubles and halves to multiply.

- Support mental calculations using jottings.

How you could plan this unit

	Stage 1	Stage 2	Stage 3	Stage 4	Stage 5
Content and vocabulary	Relationships between mathematical operations *add, subtract, multiply, divide, lots of, altogether, increase, sum, total, times, multiplied by, once, twice, three times and so on*	Using doubling and halving to multiply two-digit numbers *double, halve, twice, share equally*	Using jottings to support multiplication *jotting, method, calculate, number sentence*	Using jottings to support division	
Notes	Resource page A		Resource page B	Resource page C	

Relationships between mathematical operations

Oral/mental starter p 185

Advance Organiser

We are going to look at how the operations of addition, subtraction, multiplication and division are related

You will need: resource page A (one per child and one enlarged)

Whole-class work

- Look at the first row of resource page A together.
- Check the vocabulary.
- *What does repeat mean? What do reverse and operation mean in the context of maths?*
- Look at the second row (these are the four operations).
- *What does the third row show us?*
- *Give me a sentence to describe how A is related to B.*
- Repeat for A to C, C to D and B to D.
- Remind the children that you will be looking for more sentences to describe these relationships in the plenary session.
- Complete the next row together with the children writing what they think should go into each cell on resource page A.

Independent, paired or group work

- Ask the children to complete the remainder of resource page A.
- *Use the empty rows to make some examples of your own.*

Plenary

- *Can anyone make a sentence to describe the relationship between multiplication and addition?*
- Take lots of different suggestions and write them on the board. For example: *they both do the same thing in different ways*, and so on.
- *Why might multiplication be better to use than addition?*
- *Can anyone make a sentence to describe the relationship between multiplication and division?*
- *How could we use this relationship?*
- Suggestions might include the prompt checking of answers, using table facts and so on.
- *We know 8 × 5 = 40, so we know that there are 8 fives or 5 eights in 40, so we know that 43 ÷ 8 = 5 and a bit, and 43 ÷ 5 = 8 and a bit, and so on.*
- *Can anyone make a sentence to describe the relationship between division and subtraction?*
- *How could we use this relationship?*
- Give the children calculations and ask them to check with the inverse, or find a quicker way to work out the answer. For example, ask for the answer to 17 × 5, and then look for 85 ÷ 5 = 17; say 32 + 32 + 32 + 32 = ? and look for 4 × 32 = 128.

Name: _____

Repeating and reversing

Repeating the operation		Reversing the operation	
Multiplication	Addition	Division	Subtraction
A 24 × 4 = 96	B 24 + 24 + 24 + 24 =	C 96 ÷ 4 = 24	D 96 − 24 = 72 72 − 24 = 48 48 − 24 = 24 24 − 24 = 0
	33 + 33 + 33 = 99		
		65 ÷ 5 = 13	
			72 − 18 = 54 54 − 18 = 36 36 − 18 = 18 18 − 18 = 0
5 × 34 =			
	27 + 27 + 27 =		
		108 ÷ 27 =	
			125 − 25 = 100 100 − 25 = 75 75 − 25 = 50 50 − 25 = 25 25 − 25 = 0

Classworks © Classworks Numeracy author team, Nelson Thornes Ltd, 2003

Using doubling and halving to multiply two-digit numbers

Advance Organiser

We are going to look at how we can use doubling and halving to help us to multiply and divide

Oral/mental starter
p 185

Whole-class work

- Draw on the board the diagram shown.

- Ask the children to help you explain what it means. Then ask them to follow each 'route' and find the answer at the end.

- *Can anyone explain why we end with the same number?*

- Discuss the fact that the same answer has been arrived at using different operations.

- Repeat for a different start number, such as 9, multiplying by 6, and also by 3 and 2 (multiply by 3, then double).

- Draw a similar diagram to illustrate using halving, as shown.

- Work through the different 'routes'.

- *Can anyone explain why we end with the same number?*

- Repeat using 8 × 5 and 8 × 10 halved.

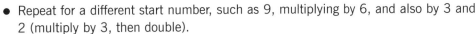

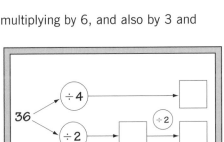

Independent, paired or group work

- Ask the children to make up their own alternative routes for the following operations: 9 × 8, 7 × 14, 22 × 8 and so on.

- Give the children similar diagrams in which they have the start and end numbers (such as 8 and 64) and have to find different operations to fill in the middle.

- Ask early finishers to make up their own alternative-routes problems for their partner.

Plenary

- Ask the children to demonstrate the examples they have made up.

- Ask the children how they could use what they have learnt. Answers might include:
  - The best way of finding an answer often depends on the numbers in the calculation.
  - Different people will have preferred methods for mental calculations. There might be more efficient methods than their preferred method so we need to be able to experience other methods to be able to compare them and then, perhaps, change the methods we use.
  - Having more than one method is good for checking answers.

Using jottings to support multiplication

Advance Organiser

We are going to make jottings to help us multiply and record our work

Oral/mental starter p 185

You will need: resource page B (enlarged)

Whole-class work

- Go through the example on resource page B with the children.

- Ask the children to explain different parts of the calculation and confirm what happens at each stage.

- Ask for alternative methods of approximation (if necessary, explain that an approximation is not just a guess but a good guess, informed by facts we know).

- Invite the children to put an approximation for 33 × 8 on the board.

- *How has 33 been partitioned into 30 and 3?*

- Check that the children can partition, by asking for random examples of numbers between 10 and 99 and then using those examples to partition.

- Demonstrate, with a second calculation, asking the children to help you work similarly to the example on resource page B.

- Complete more examples together, if necessary.

Independent, paired or group work

- Ask the children to answer the following questions using the method above: 17 × 8, 23 × 6, 27 × 8, 37 × 4, 43 × 6, 53 × 7, 57 × 9, 63 × 4.

- When you feel that the children are ready, encourage them to use their own words to describe the different stages of the process to you, an adult or a partner.

- Ask them to work together to make posters of one of their answers, showing the working, and explaining what they did at each stage.

Plenary

- Set up a gallery presentation (that is, stick examples up around the walls) of the posters the children have made and give everyone a few minutes to look around the gallery.

- *Did anyone see something that was set out very differently from their own?*

- Ask the children to demonstrate how they worked out their answers.

- *Does anybody have another way of doing these sorts of calculations?*

- Share these alternative ideas – can they be used for every example? What are the relative merits of the different ways?

EXAMPLE

Explaining work

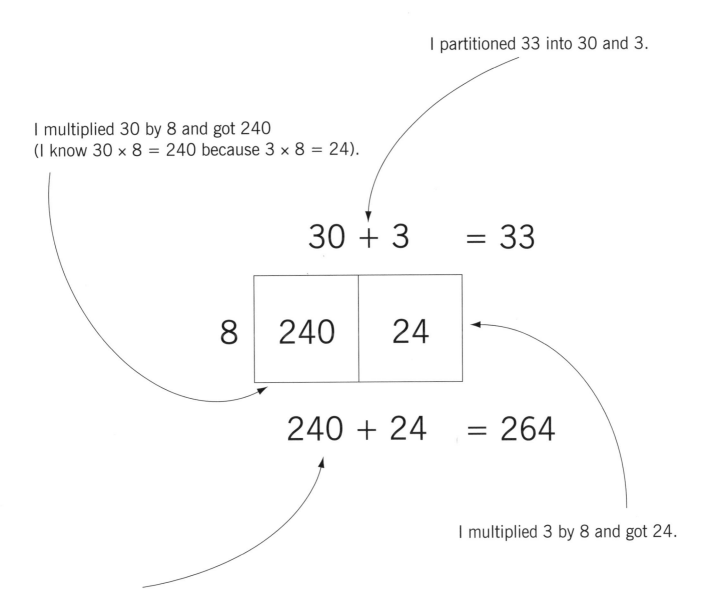

I partitioned 33 into 30 and 3.

I multiplied 30 by 8 and got 240
(I know 30 × 8 = 240 because 3 × 8 = 24).

30 + 3   = 33

| 8 | 240 | 24 |

240 + 24   = 264

I multiplied 3 by 8 and got 24.

I added 240 (8 lots of 30) and 24 (8 lots of 3)
and got 264 (8 lots of 33).

Classworks © Classworks Numeracy author team, Nelson Thornes Ltd, 2003

Using jottings to support division

Oral/mental starter
p 185

Advance Organiser

We are going to use jottings to divide and to record our work

You will need: resource page C

Whole-class work

- Go through the example on resource page C together, by drawing the example on a board/flipchart.

- Work through each stage, ensuring the children understand what happens at each point.

- Ask the children to suggest alternative methods of approximation (if necessary, explain that an approximation is not just a guess but a 'good guess', informed by facts we know).

- Encourage the children to put an approximation for 62 divided by 5 on the board.

- Ask the children for ways of partitioning 62.

- Demonstrate partitioning into 60 and 2.

- Complete the problem using different methods of partitioning.

- Check that the children can partition by asking for random examples of numbers between 10 and 99 and then using those examples to partition in a variety of ways.

- Ask the children to suggest how they would describe each part of the example to a partner.

- Complete more examples together, if necessary.

Independent, paired or group work

- Ask the children to use similar methods to complete 47 ÷ 5, 67 ÷ 5, 73 ÷ 8, 78 ÷ 5, 86 ÷ 6, 53 ÷ 4 or 67 ÷ 9.

Plenary

- Ask the children to work in pairs to demonstrate the method they have used and record what they did.

- *Did anyone do anything different? How can we check that answer?*

Name: _____

Explaining work

$$62 \div 5$$

Approximation: $60 \div 5 = 12$

$62 \div 5 =$ ◄———————— So $62 \div 5$ must be between

12 and 13

$65 \div 5 = 13$

Calculate: $60 + 2 = 62$ ◄———— Partition 62 into a multiple of 5

and whatever is left over

$60 \div 5 = 12$ ◄

2 left over ◄——————— Solve each part separately

$62 \div 5 = 12$ remainder 2 ◄———— Add the answers together

Classworks © Classworks Numeracy author team, Nelson Thornes Ltd, 2003

Multiplication and Division (2)

Outcome

Children will be able to understand some of the laws relating to multiplication, and different written and mental methods for solving multiplication calculations

Medium-term plan objectives

- Understand commutative and associative laws of multiplication.
- Divide a whole number of pounds by 2, 4, 5 or 10 to give £p.
- Use closely related facts; for example, derive multiply by 9 or 11 from multiply by 10, or derive 6 times-table from 4 times-table plus 2 times-table.
- Partition and multiply.
- Develop and refine written methods for TU × U.

Overview

- Understand that, for example, 6 × 3 has the same value as 3 × 6.
- Understand that, for example, (6 × 3) × 5 has the same value as 6 × (3 × 5).
- Divide whole number amounts of pounds into pounds and pence.
- Develop and use more complex written methods where appropriate.

How you could plan this unit

	Stage 1	Stage 2	Stage 3	Stage 4	Stage 5
Content and vocabulary	Understanding commutative laws applying to multiplication *lots of, groups of, times, product, multiply, multiplied by, multiple of, once, twice, three times and so on, array, row, column, double, halve, symbol, value, number sentence*	Understanding associative laws applying to multiplication	Dividing amounts of money *share, share equally, equal groups of, money, coin, note, pay, change*	Developing written methods for multiplication *jotting, method, answer, how did you work it out?, calculate, calculation*	
Notes	Resource page A				

Understanding commutative laws applying to multiplication

Advance Organiser

We are going to investigate the fact that $3 \times 4 = 4 \times 3$

Oral/mental starter
p 185

You will need: resource page A (one per child and one enlarged, or on an OHT), multiplication square from 1 to 10 on each axis

Whole-class work

- Show the children a copy of resource page A.

- Complete the first three lines of the multiplication chart together.

- *Who can draw a diagram to show that 3×4 has the same value as 4×3?*

- Prompt with an array if necessary, encouraging the children to draw a 4×3 array, then turn it through 90 degrees to illustrate a 3×4 array.

- Draw a multiplication square on the board or show the children one enlarged or on an OHT.

- Point to or highlight the product *12* of the multiplication 4×3.

- *How did the person who made the square know which number to put in this box?*

- *What number sentence gives me this answer? Who can tell me another one?*

- Demonstrate reading down and then across, and across then down, then point to the diagonally adjacent *12* and ask children the same questions.

×	1	2	3	4	5
1	1	2	3	4	5
2	2	4	6	8	10
3	3	6	9	12	15
4	4	8	12	16	20

Independent, paired or group work

- Give the children a copy of resource page A.

- *Complete the multiplication chart, making up some examples of your own to fill in the empty rows of the chart.*

- *Can anyone find an example where the answers to the two calculations are not the same?*

Plenary

- Discuss the children's work on resource page A.

- Look at the multiplication square on the board.

- Choose numbers at random and ask the children to tell you number sentences for various numbers on the square.

- *Who can think of number sentences that give the same product, but that are not on the square?*

- *Help me to continue the square.*

Name: _____

Multiplication chart

Complete the multiplication chart making up some examples of your own to fill in the empty rows of the chart.

Can anyone find an example where the answers to the two calculations are not the same?

2 × 9 =	9 × 2 =
3 × 4 =	4 × 3 =
4 × 7 =	7 × 4 =
5 × 9 =	9 × 5 =
11 × 6 =	6 × 11 =
12 × 7 =	7 × 12 =
15 × 5 =	5 × 15 =
24 × 4 =	4 × 24 =
25 × 7 =	7 × 25 =
31 × 4 =	4 × 31 =
35 × 8 =	8 × 35 =

Classworks © Classworks Numeracy author team, Nelson Thornes Ltd, 2003

Understanding associative laws applying to multiplication

Advance Organiser

We are going to investigate why 6 × (3 × 5) has the same value as (6 × 3) × 5

Oral/mental starter p 185

Whole-class work

- Write on the board: 6 × *(3 × 5)*.

- *Can somebody read the statement?*

- *Who can tell me what the brackets mean? Who can tell me the answer?*

- Work through multiplying 3 × 5 first, to get 15, then 6 × 15 to get 90.

- *Who can tell me another way to solve this calculation?*

- Introduce the idea, if no one suggests it, of first calculating 6 × 3, then multiplying the answer by 5.

- *Will we get the same answer, or a different one? Why do you think that?*

- Draw on the board the following illustration of the working and discuss it with the children.

- You might find it useful to try an easier example to test that this is *not* a trick that applies to just these numbers, for example: 3 × 6 = 3 × (2 × 3)

- *Can somebody read the statement?*

- *Why is this part of the statement true?*

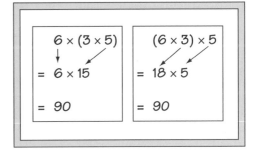

Independent, paired or group work

- Ask the children to investigate solving 7 × (2 × 6) and (7 × 2) × 6, 6 × (2 × 8) and (6 × 2) × 8 and so on, each time recording how they solve each stage of the problem.

- More able children can investigate, for example, breaking 9 × 18 into 9 × (3 × 6) and therefore (9 × 3) × 6.

Plenary

- Look at some of the examples that the children have created.

- *Which was the easiest problem to solve each time?*

- Look at some of the more able children's examples. Then discuss breaking 6 × 42 into 6 × (6 × 7) and how this might help them solve the problem.

- Focus the children on the fact that the different number sentences have the *same value*, and point out the use of the '=' symbol to indicate this.

Dividing amounts of money

Oral/mental starter
p 185

Advance Organiser

We are going to find out how to share amounts of pounds into pounds and pence

Whole-class work

- Draw the beginnings of a table on the board as shown.

- Encourage the children to talk about the context; for example, a lottery or prize draw.

- Indicate the first cell.

- *How do we know what to put in here?*

Prize money	Number of winners			
÷	2	4	5	10
£17				
£23				

- Encourage the children to think about ways of solving £17 ÷ 2. Point out, if necessary, that although 17 is an odd number of pounds, they know that there are 100 pence in £1.

- Accept a range of responses and write them on the board. Encourage responses based on real life and that keep the amounts 'whole' in pounds and pence, rather than in terms of fractions.

- For example, £17 has the same value as £16 + £1, and £16 divided by 2 is £8 and £1 divided by 2 is 50p, so the answer is £8.50.

- Model giving 'change' for £1 as two 50p coins if necessary.

- *How do we write the answer to this problem?*

- Look for an awareness that the question deals with money, and encourage children to write £8.50 rather than £8.50p.

- Work quickly through the next example (£17 ÷ 4), raising the same points and asking if the children can use the answer to the first calculation to get the answer to the second. Other methods might involve sharing £16 into four groups of £4, then sharing the £1 left over into four groups of 25p.

Independent, paired or group work

- Draw other whole-number amounts of pounds in the prize money column and ask the children to copy and complete the table.

Plenary

- Compare answers from different children and check that they are all written with the correct notation.

- Ask the children to explain how they worked out the answer each time.

Developing written methods for multiplication

Advance Organiser

We are going to learn to multiply a two-digit number by a single-digit number using jottings

Oral/mental starter p 185

You will need: arrow place-value cards

Whole-class work

- Write on the board: *24 × 6.*

- *Who can help me estimate the answer?*

- Write on the board the calculations shown.

- *To which of these is the answer to 24 × 6 nearer? Why?*

- Use arrow cards to demonstrate partitioning 24 into 20 and 4.

- Ask the children to calculate 6 lots of 20 using various methods including counting in 20s or counting in twos and multiplying by 10.

- Suggest calculating 6 lots of 4 by doubling and doubling again.

- Combine the answers 120 and 24 to make 144.

- Demonstrate at two levels the grid method of multiplication which uses the same approach, that of partitioning.

- Demonstrate the following vertical method of recording the same calculation and talk it through with the children.

- *Six lots of 20 makes 120. Six lots of 4 makes 24. 120 plus 24 makes 144.*

$$20 \times 6 = 120$$
$$24 \times 6 =$$
$$25 \times 6 = 150$$

24
10+10+4 = 24

6 | 60 ⊕ 60 ⊕ 24 | = 144

24
20 + 4 = 24

6 | 120 ⊕ 24 | = 144

$$
\begin{array}{r}
24 \\
\times\, 6 \\
6 \times 20 = 120 \\
6 \times\ \ 4 = \ \ 24 \\
6 \times 24 = 144 \\
\end{array}
$$

Independent, paired or group work

- *Calculate the following, using your preferred method out of: arrow cards, the grid method or the vertical method. Estimate first.*

- 38 × 4, 26 × 6, 48 × 7, 59 × 3, 45 × 9, 25 × 6, 38 × 5, 54 × 4, 67 × 7, 92 × 8

Plenary

- Consider the above calculations and ask the children to explain how they worked them out.

- *Can you think of different ways of finding the answers?*

- Ask the children to demonstrate their method. Display some neatly written methods to the rest of the class.

Multiplication and Division (3)

Outcome

Children will be able to use their knowledge of multiplication and division to solve calculations and real life problems

Medium-term plan objectives	• Understand distributive law. • Round up or down after division. • Use relation between × and ÷. • Use known facts to multiply and divide. • Develop and refine written methods for TU ÷ U.
Overview	• Refine written methods of division. • Use known facts. • Solve problems in real-life contexts using rounding. • Apply place value knowledge to solving multiplication problems.

How you could plan this unit

	Stage 1	Stage 2	Stage 3	Stage 4	Stage 5
Content and vocabulary	Written methods of division *lots of, groups of, times, divide, divided by, repeated subtraction, array, row, column, jotting, method, sign, operation, symbol, equation, number sentence*	Using known facts to multiply and divide *share, share equally, group, equal groups of, divide, divided by, divided into*	Deciding whether to round up or down after division *remainder, how did you work it out?, decide, work out, solve, check*	Using the distributive law to multiply *place, place value, tens, ones, units, hundreds, one digit, two digit, three digit*	
Notes		Resource page A	Resource page B		

64

Written methods of division

Advance Organiser

We are going to learn written ways of how to divide a two-digit number by a single-digit number

Oral/mental starter p 185

Whole-class work

- Write on the board: *56 ÷ 6.*

- *Can anyone give me an approximate answer to this calculation?*

- Work through approximating an answer by encouraging the children to record that *54 ÷ 6 = 9* and *60 ÷ 6 = 10* so *56 ÷ 6 has a value between 9 and 10.*

- Ask children whether the answer will be nearer to 9 or nearer to 10, and how they know.

- Ask for suggestions as to how to solve the problem.

- *We know that there are more than 9 lots of 6 in 56, so we can take off 9 × 6 from our total.*

- Model solving the equation using repeated subtraction on a number line.

$$- (9 \times 6)$$

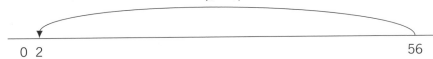

0 2   56

- Record these steps using the following format and ask the children if they can explain what each step means.

```
  56
– 54 =          (9 × 6)
   2            remainder
```

- Demonstrate using other repeated subtractions.

```
  56
– 30 =          (10 × 3)
  26
– 15 =          (5 × 3)
  11
–  9 =          (3 × 3)
   2
```

Independent, paired or group work

- Ask the children to calculate the following using an empty number line first, then a vertical format showing the relationship. Remind them to approximate first, then calculate.

  58 ÷ 4 =   62 ÷ 5 =   76 ÷ 7   94 ÷ 5=   74 ÷ 9   71 ÷ 8 =

Plenary

- Discuss the following, asking the children for ideas on how to solve them quickly: 124 ÷ 8, 96 ÷ 9, 121 ÷ 4, 562 ÷ 8.

- Ask for a volunteer to write their solution in a vertical format and another to write it as an empty number line.

Using known facts to multiply and divide

Advance Organiser

We are going to use what we already know to solve calculations

You will need: resource page A (one per child and one enlarged)

Whole-class work

- Look at the examples on resource page A with the class.

- *Who can read out this missing-number sentence?*

- For example, *7 (multiplied by, times, lots of) something equals 63.*

- *Who can tell me a story for this missing-number sentence?*

- If necessary, give an example: *Seven people paid the same price each for a ticket to the theatre. £63 was the total price. How much did they each pay?*

- *How could we solve this problem?*

- Encourage the children to visualise the problem and what is happening. Watch out for them picking up words such as 'total' that could mislead them. Ask for ideas and write them on the board.

- Encourage the children to consider finding the missing number through their knowledge of the times-tables (*I know that 63 is 7 nines*) or we could use the inverse operation (*If 7 × a missing number = 63 then 63 ÷ 7 = the missing number*).

- Repeat the process for the other examples.

Independent, paired or group work

- Ask the children to find the other missing numbers on resource page A.

Plenary

- Give feedback on the children's responses to the exercise on resource page A.

- Ask the children to report on the methods they used.

- *Did you use the same method for every example?*

- Try some other examples, discussing the methods that could be used each time.

- $7 \times \square = 56$; $\square \times 9 = 99$; $6 \times \square = 132$; $\square \times 9 = 108$; $63 \div \square = 9$; $\square \div 8 = 7$; $135 \div \square = 9$; $\square \div 7 = 14$.

Name: _____

Find the missing number

$7 \times \boxed{} = 63$	$8 \times \boxed{} = 72$	$6 \times \boxed{} = 36$
$5 \times \boxed{} = 45$	$9 \times \boxed{} = 54$	$6 \times \boxed{} = 54$
$\boxed{} \times 7 = 49$	$\boxed{} \times 8 = 72$	$\boxed{} \times 9 = 63$
$\boxed{} \times 3 = 27$	$\boxed{} \times 7 = 42$	$\boxed{} \times 9 = 81$
$9 \times \boxed{} = 108$	$8 \times \boxed{} = 112$	$6 \times \boxed{} = 96$
$7 \times \boxed{} = 119$	$8 \times \boxed{} = 128$	$6 \times \boxed{} = 126$
$\boxed{} \times 7 = 84$	$\boxed{} \times 8 = 104$	$\boxed{} \times 9 = 117$
$45 \div \boxed{} = 9$	$63 \div \boxed{} = 7$	$54 \div \boxed{} = 9$
$72 \div \boxed{} = 9$	$56 \div \boxed{} = 7$	$81 \div \boxed{} = 9$
$\boxed{} \div 7 = 5$	$\boxed{} \div 6 = 9$	$\boxed{} \div 8 = 8$
$\boxed{} \div 9 = 5$	$\boxed{} \div 4 = 7$	$\boxed{} \div 8 = 7$
$135 \div \boxed{} = 9$	$154 \div \boxed{} = 7$	$144 \div \boxed{} = 9$
$\boxed{} \div 9 = 12$	$\boxed{} \div 4 = 15$	$\boxed{} \div 8 = 14$

Deciding whether to round up or down after division

Advance Organiser

We are going to decide how to solve problems in the real world involving division

You will need: resource page B

Whole-class work

- Read the children the following problem.

- *A troop of 39 scouts is going on camp. They have tents that can sleep six people. How many tents will they need?*

- Ask the children to close their eyes and visualise the problem. Encourage them to think about what is happening: is something being grouped, or added together, or shared out?

- Ask the children to explain in their own words what the problem is and how they could solve it.

- Draw on the board the diagram shown.

- *What do you think this shows? How does it help you to visualise the problem? Who can explain what we are doing?*

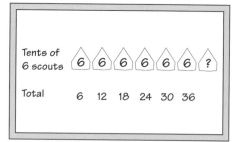

- Encourage the children to imagine the 39 scouts grouped into tents of six scouts each. Ask the children to help you carry out the grouping.

- *We have grouped 36 scouts into six tents. We have three scouts left. How many more tents do we need?*

- Point out that although the seventh tent will not be full, we still need the whole tent in the real world. Confirm that the answer to the problem is *seven tents*.

- Pose the following problem, involving the same numbers and ostensibly the same operation.

- *John has collected 39 stamps. Each page in his stamp album will hold six stamps. How many pages can he fill completely?*

- Discuss the problem with the children. Ask them to visualise it and repeat the steps above, concluding that, although there will be three stamps left over, he can only fill six pages completely. The answer to the problem is *six full pages*.

Independent, paired or group work

- Ask the children to work in pairs. Give each pair one or more problems from resource page B.

- Encourage them to record their work and how they visualised the problem.

Plenary

- Using the following word problem, ask the children to help you solve it and to explain each stage of the process, providing alternative methods where they can.

- *Fifteen friends are staying in a hotel. They want to go into the centre of the city by taxi. The hotel porter knows that the taxi can only take four people. How many taxis does he need to summon?*

Name: _____

Solve the problems

1 Eggs are packed in boxes of six. How many boxes will be needed to store 41 eggs?

2 85 people from a school are going on a trip to a museum. They want to order buses to take them. The bus company has buses that can carry a maximum of 25 passengers. How many buses will be needed?

3 Three friends go out for a meal in a pizza restaurant and decide to split the bill equally between them. The bill is £24.23. How much should each person pay?

4 Eight wheels are needed to make a pair of roller blades. How many pairs can be made with 60 wheels?

5 Aftab, Dave, Ernie, June and Grace work together baking biscuits. When the baking is done there are 53 biscuits. They want to share them equally. How many biscuits should each of the friends get?

Classworks © Classworks Numeracy author team, Nelson Thornes Ltd, 2003

Using the distributive law to multiply

Advance Organiser

We are going to learn to multiply numbers by partitioning and recombining

Oral/mental starter p 185

You will need: arrow place-value cards

Whole-class work

- Practise using arrow cards to partition a selection of two-digit numbers.

- After trying a few, write the last two-digit number you partitioned on the board.

- *We partitioned 36 into 30 and 6. How could that help us multiply 36 by 7?*

- Point out that we can multiply each part of 36 separately and then add the answers together.

- Write this on the board, as shown.

- Repeat for 24 × 9, ensuring the children can tell you what happens at every stage.

- *Who can partition 24 into tens and ones? How many tens? So what is 9 × 20? What do we do next?*

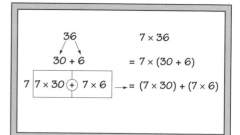

Independent, paired or group work

- Ask the children to use partitioning to solve some of the following problems:

  35 × 7, 28 × 4, 46 × 6, 32 × 5, 48 × 7, 54 × 6, 27 × 8, 31 × 9, 56 × 3, 76 × 6, 51 × 4, 73 × 5.

Plenary

- Go through some of the children's work with the class.

- *Who can tell me how we could multiply three-digit numbers?*

- Challenge children to help you design a grid to help you solve 163 × 7.

Solving Problems (1)

Outcome

Children will be able to apply appropriate methods and operations to solve word problems involving money

Medium-term plan objectives	• Convert pounds to pence. • Choose appropriate number operations and calculation methods to solve money or 'real life' word problems with one or two steps. • Explain and record method. • Check with addition in a different order.
Overview	• Convert pounds to pence. • Listen carefully to word problems. • Choose appropriate operations and methods to solve problems with one step. • Use trial-and-improvement methods. • Check results by adding in a different order.

How you could plan this unit

	Stage 1	Stage 2	Stage 3	Stage 4	Stage 5
Content and vocabulary	Converting amounts of pounds to pence *money, coin, note, penny, pence, pound, £, pay, change, how much?, total, amount, value*	Solving one-step problems involving money *lots of, groups of, multiply, multiplied, divided, divide, share, equals, estimate, approximate, accurate, exact*	Solving pounds and pence problems and checking results *multiply, multiplied, divided, divide, share, equals, estimate, approximate, accurate, exact, addition, add, subtract*		
Notes	Confirm children are aware that there are 100 pence in £1. Practise changing amounts of pounds into amounts of pence, then converting £p amounts to pence. Demonstrate using coins.	Resource page A	Resource page B		

Solving one-step problems involving money

Advance Organiser

We are going to find out how many lengths Parveen completed in the sponsored swim

Oral/mental starter pp 185–186

You will need: resource page A (one per child and one enlarged)

Whole-class work

- Read out the following word problem to the children. Ask them to close their eyes and visualise the problem as you read it out.

- *Parveen takes part in a sponsored swim. His aunt sponsors him 5p per length. When he finishes the sponsored swim, his aunt gives him £1.75. How many lengths did Parveen swim?*

- Ask the children to think carefully about the problem and to explain in their own words what the problem is asking them, and how they could solve it.

- Establish that £1.75 is the same as 175p.

- Write some ideas on the board. Encourage the children to visualise either the amounts of 5p repeating until they make £1.75 altogether, or the £1.75 being grouped into lots of 5p, and to relate this to the number of lengths.

- Lead the children towards the idea that they need to find how many lots of 5p make £1.75, and *ask them to explain how they could do this.*

- Introduce the idea that the children can use what they know to make a good guess or estimate. Ask for suggestions from the children and record them on the board.

- *David said that 10 lots of 5p makes 50p. How does this help us?*

- *Amy thought the answer could be 50 lengths. How can we check? What is 50 times 5p? How did you work that out?*

- *Cheryl, you think that 30 lots of 5p makes £1.50 so the answer must be more than 30. Martin says that 40 lots of 5p makes £2.00 so the answer must be less than 40.* Record each estimate and begin to narrow down the answers.

- Encourage the children to progress to working out the final answer.

- *We know the answer must be between 30 and 40. Who wants to make a closer guess? Will the answer be closer to 30 or closer to 40? Why do you think that?*

- Continue to use trial-and-improvement to narrow the answer down to 35 lengths.

Independent, paired or group work

- Ask the children to complete the rest of the word problems on resource page A.

Plenary

- Invite some of the children to the front of the class to show how they found their answers.

- Work through some examples with the class.

- *Who had a different answer? Who used a different method?* Ensure that those who misunderstood the problem know what they should have done.

Name: _____

Solving money problems

1 Katie swam 12 lengths in the sponsored swim and earned a total of £2.40.

   How much was she sponsored per length?

2 Michael was sponsored 16p by his dad for each length he completed. He completed

   32 lengths. How much should he get in total?

3 Abi received £2.56 from her big sister for completing 16 lengths. How much was she

   sponsored for each length?

4 Anwar received £4.05 in total for his part of the sponsored swim. How much might he

   have been sponsored per length? How many lengths might he have swum? Write as

   many answers as you can.

Classworks © Classworks Numeracy author team, Nelson Thornes Ltd, 2003

Solving pounds and pence problems and checking results

Advance Organiser

We are going to solve problems involving money

You will need: coins, resource page B (one per child)

Whole-class work

- Read out the following word problem to the children. Ask them to close their eyes and visualise the problem as you read it out.

- *Colin has one of every silver coin except for 5p coins. He has two 2p coins. He has one of the least valuable coins. His sister gives him two 20p coins. How much does he have altogether?*

- Ask the children to think carefully about the problem and to explain in their own words what the problem is asking them, and how they could solve it.

- Discuss the amount of information in the problem. Encourage the children to think of ways to organise this information so that they can find the total more easily.

- Demonstrate using a table, such as the following, if no one suggests a similar method.

- Encourage the children to check with the information in the word problem. Suggest that they write down notes about each coin and check carefully against the table.

Coins	Number of coins	Amount of money
5p	0	0p
10p	1	10p
20p	3	60p
50p	1	50p
2p	2	4p
1p	1	1p

- Work through, totalling the coins with the class.

- Show them how to check the addition by adding the coins in a different order.

Independent, paired or group work

- Ask the children to complete resource page B.

- Support the children by giving them coins to match to the problems.

Plenary

- Invite the children to demonstrate how they solved some of the problems on resource page B.

- Point out techniques for adding and checking the addition, and suggest using multiplication where appropriate.

Name: _____

Solving money problems

Work out how much money each child has altogether.

I have one
£2 coin, two 50p coins, one
10p coin, five 20p coins, two 5p
coins, one 10p coin and five 2p
coins. How much do I have
altogether?

I have five
20p coins and two 10p
coins. Billy gives me two 2p
coins, one 1p coin, two 20p coins
and one 10p coin. How much
do I have now?

I have £1
made up of 20p coins.
Mary gives me one 50p coin,
one 5p coin and one 10p coin.
How much do I have
altogether?

Jonny has a
2p coin, one £1 and one
£2 coin, 10p made up of 5p
coins and one 50p coin. He finds
five 20p coins and another 50p
coin. How much in total?

Margaret has
five of each kind of coin from
1p to 50p. She loses two 1p coins,
three 2p coins, one 5p coin, two 10p
coins, a 20p coin and four 50p
coins. How much does she
have now?

Classworks © Classworks Numeracy author team, Nelson Thornes Ltd, 2003

Solving Problems (2)

Outcome

Children will be able to solve problems and check them using the equivalent calculation

Medium-term plan objectives	• Choose appropriate number operations and calculation methods to solve money and 'real life' word problems with one or more steps.
	• Explain and record methods.
	• Check with equivalent calculation.

Overview	• Work out doubles and trebles and check results.
	• Combine information to solve problems.
	• Solve more complex problems in real-life contexts.

How you could plan this unit

	Stage 1	Stage 2	Stage 3	Stage 4	Stage 5
Content and vocabulary	Choosing methods and checking results *single, once, double, twice, two times, treble, three times, multiply, add, subtract, take away, order*	Solving word problems and checking results *single, once, double, twice, two times, treble, three times, multiply, add, subtract, take away, order*	Solving money problems *money, coin, note, penny, pence, pound, £, price, cost*		
Notes	Resource page A	Resource page B	Set the children money problems involving multiple steps and different operations; for example, 'Finding the total spent on four oranges at 12p each, six lemons at 18p each and a mango at 67p. They pay with a £2 coin. How much change?'		

Choosing methods and checking results

Oral/mental starter pp 185–186

Advance Organiser

We are going to find a total score and check our result

You will need: dartboard, resource page A (one per child and one for you)

Whole-class work

- Show the children a dartboard and explain that three darts are thrown in a game of darts.

- Ask them if they can describe what scores come from different parts of the board.

- Explain, if necessary, that the outside ring means every dart scores double the number for that section and that the inner ring means every dart scores treble the number for that section.

- *Who can tell me what 'treble' means?*

- *Deepak threw three darts. One landed on 16, one on double 14 and one on treble 20. How much did he score altogether?*

- Indicate the areas of the board and ask the children to visualise how they can solve the problem.

- Encourage them to suggest ways of solving the problem. Suggest some method of recording the information, either informal jottings or a table of some kind.

- Demonstrate the following different methods as appropriate.

Area	Number	×	Score
Single	16	× 1	16
Double	14	× 2	28
Treble	20	× 3	60

$(16 \times 1) + (14 \times 2) + (20 \times 3)$
$= 16 + 28 + 60$
$= 10 + 20 + 60 + 6 + 8$
$= 90 + 14$
$= 104$

- Agree on a preferred method and ask the children to help you work through it.

- How can we check our answer? What is another way to solve the problem?

- Show the children how to check the total by adding the numbers in a different order. For example, 16 + double 14 + treble 20 could be checked as 16 + 14 + 14 + 20 + 20 + 20. Include checking individual scores, such as checking 17×3 by doing $(10 \times 3) + (7 \times 3)$.

- Repeat for another three-dart score.

Independent, paired or group work

- Ask the children to complete resource page A.

Plenary

- Invite the children to explain how they solved some of the problems.

- *How could you check that multiplication/addition?*

- Give some more examples of checking using calculations that they know have the same value. For example, checking 14×2 using $(10 \times 2) + (4 \times 2)$, or checking 18×3 using $(10 \times 3) + (8 \times 3)$.

Name: _____

Finding the total score

Find the total score for each child.

1 Carrie hit double 7, treble 4 and single 19.

2 Momoko hit single 17, double 13 and double 15.

3 Ahmed hit double 16, treble 17 and the other dart missed.

4 Barney hit double 9, double 13 and treble 19.

5 Tamsin hit 14, double 20 and treble 20.

6 Sofi hit treble 16, double 16 and double 9.

Solving word problems and checking results

Advance Organiser

We are going to work out the missing scores and check our answers

Oral/mental starter
pp 185–186

You will need: dartboard or drawing of one, resource page B (one per child and one for you)

Whole-class work

- Show the children the dartboard and explain that three darts are thrown. Explain that doubles are scored when the darts hit the outer ring and trebles are scored when the darts hit the inner ring. Tell the children that the inner bull's-eye scores 50 points and the outer bull's-eye 25 points.

- Encourage them to note the scores for each part of the board.

- *Sally scored 46 in total. Her first dart was a single 14 and her second dart was a double 7. What was her last dart?*

- Ask children to visualise the problem and to suggest ways of solving it. Write some on the board. Encourage the children to use jottings or a more formal method of recording the information to help them.

- Suggest a table, if necessary, such as the one shown.

- Solve the problem with the children; for example, by adding 14 and double 7 (or multiplying 7 by 4, or adding two lots of 14) to make 28, then subtracting 28 from 46. Discuss every stage with the class.

Area	Number	×	Score
Single	14	× 1	14
Double	7	× 2	14
....	....	....	....
Total			46

- *We have 18 points left. How could I score 18 on this board?*

- Record the various possibilities: treble 6, double 9, single 18.

Independent, paired or group work

- Ask the children to complete resource page B.

- Support the children by using a table showing the products of the numbers 1 to 20 when multiplied by 2 and 3.

- Early finishers could explore the range of numbers that cannot be scored with two doubles or two trebles.

Plenary

- Invite the children to explain how they solved some of the puzzles.

- *Where did you start? Why?*

- *How could you check that multiplication/addition?*

- Show them how to solve and check multiplication using an equivalent calculation; for example, 19 × 3 has the same value as 10 × 3 add 9 × 3.

(**PUPIL PAGE**)

Name: _____

Finding the missing scores

Complete the missing scores for each child.

First dart: double 19

1 Shelly scored 97 in total. Her first dart hit double 19 and her second dart scored 39.

Second dart: ☐

Third dart: ☐

First dart: ☐

2 Marvin scored 78 in total. His second dart scored 14 and his third dart scored 45. What did his first dart score? Where might it have landed on the board?

Second dart: ☐

Third dart: ☐

First dart: ☐

3 Gaia scored 59 in total. Her first dart was a treble and scored 36. Her second dart was a double 7. What did the first dart land on? Where might her third dart have landed?

Second dart: ☐

Third dart: ☐

First dart: ☐

4 Malcolm throws one dart into treble 20 and another dart into double 18. He needs to score 110 exactly to win and his last dart has to be a double. Where should he aim?

Second dart: ☐

Third dart: ☐

First dart: ☐

5 Vivek needs to score exactly 156 to win. If his third dart has to be a double, what scores could he make for each throw?

Second dart: ☐

Third dart: ☐

Classworks © Classworks Numeracy author team, Nelson Thornes Ltd, 2003

Solving Problems (3)

Outcome

Children will be able to select and apply different approaches to word problems

Medium-term plan objectives

- Choose appropriate number operations and calculation methods to solve money and 'real life' word problems with one or more steps.
- Explain working.
- Check with an equivalent calculation.

Overview

- Use diagrams to solve word problems.
- Check work using equivalent calculations.
- Select methods and operations to solve 'real life' word problems.
- Explain working and check results.

How you could plan this unit

	Stage 1	Stage 2	Stage 3	Stage 4	Stage 5
Content and vocabulary	Solving word problems using jottings and diagrams *inverse, equivalent, add, subtract, multiply, divide*	Choosing methods and operations to solve calculations			
Notes	Resource page A	Resource page B			

Solving word problems using jottings and diagrams

Advance Organiser

We are going to find the mystery number

You will need: resource page A (one per child and one for you)

Whole-class work

- *I'm thinking of a number. I multiply the number by 5 and then add 11 to make 71. Which number was I thinking of?*

- Encourage the children to imagine what happens as you say the words. Ask them to describe in their own words what happens.

- If necessary, provide the following diagram.

- Ask the children what should go in each part of the diagram. Discuss how it relates to the word problem.

- Write *71* in the last box, *+ 11* in the box before that, and × 5 in the small box before that.

- *Who can help me solve this now? What do we do first?*

- Encourage the children to perform the inverse operation. Draw a diagram beneath the one already on the board to demonstrate *subtracting 11* to get to 60, then *dividing by 5* to get to the start number, 12.

- *How can we check our work?*

- Encourage the children to check those stages they are unsure of and then to work through the problem beginning with 12.

- Repeat for the following problem: *I think of a number, add 6 then multiply by 8 to get 72.*

Independent, paired or group work

- Ask the children to complete resource page A.

Plenary

- Invite the children to explain how they solved some of the problems.

- *What equivalent calculation could you use to check that?*

- Take suggestions of equivalent calculations.

- Give some examples, such as, explain that *adding 99* is equivalent to *adding 100 and then subtracting 1*. Explain that *equivalent to* means *has the same value as* because 100 subtract 1 equals 99.

- Explain that multiplying by 6 is equivalent to multiplying by 3 and then doubling.

- Explain that multiplying by 4 is equivalent to doubling and then doubling again.

- *How could you multiply by 8?*

Name: _____

Solving problems

Solve these problems and show how each part of the problem could be solved or checked using an equivalent calculation.

1 I think of a number. I multiply my number by 4 and then add 19 to make 63.

   How I checked _____

2 I think of a number. I multiply my number by 4 and then add 19 to make 107.

   How I checked _____

3 I think of a number. I add 9 and then multiply by 4 to make 48.

   How I checked _____

4 I think of a number. I divide my number by 6 and then add 99 to make 105.

   How I checked _____

5 I think of a number. I subtract 34 and then divide by 8 to make 6.

   How I checked _____

Classworks © Classworks Numeracy author team, Nelson Thornes Ltd, 2003

Choosing methods and operations to solve calculations

Oral/mental starter
pp 185–186

Advance Organiser

We are going to decide how to solve a word problem and then solve it

You will need: resource page B (one per child and one for you)

Whole-class work

- *Robert and Leah have 66 marbles altogether. Robert has twice as many marbles as Leah. How many do they each have?*

- Ask the children to listen carefully to the problem with their eyes closed. Encourage them to explain in their own words what happens at each stage. Take ideas as to how to solve the problem. Encourage the children to break the problem into stages.

- *Robert has twice as many marbles as Leah. There are 66 marbles in total.*

- Encourage visual solutions to the problem. If necessary, or if suggested, model the problem using cubes or counters.

- Draw the following diagram on the board to illustrate the problem.

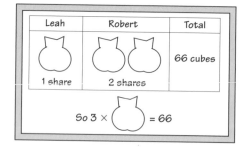

- Leah has one share of the marbles but Robert has twice as many, so he has two shares the same size. So we need to share 66 marbles into three equal shares.

- Draw out that *66 shared by 3 makes 22.*

- Sum up: *Leah gets one share (22) and Robert has two shares (22 + 22 = 44).*

- Repeat for: *Candy and Omar have 45 marbles altogether. Candy has half as many marbles as Omar. How many do they each have?*

- Ensure that the children realise this is a different question. Encourage them to see that they solve it in a similar way, because if Candy has half as many as Omar, that is equivalent to saying that Omar has twice as many as Candy.

Independent, paired or group work

- Ask the children to complete resource page B.

- The last two questions will stretch early finishers.

Plenary

- Invite the children to explain how they solved some of the problems. Encourage them to share any diagrams, jottings or other working.

- *How could you check that with an equivalent calculation?*

- Ask the children some quick-fire questions involving equivalent calculations.

Name: _____

Solving problems

Solve each problem and write down equivalent calculations that can be used to check your work.

1   Ahmed and Anna have 33 marbles altogether. Anna has twice as many marbles as Ahmed. How many do they each have?

2   Judy and Soraya have 93 conkers altogether. Soraya has all but 30 of the conkers. How many do they each have?

3   Maliha and Tunde have 72 counters altogether. Tunde has half as many counters as Maliha. How many do they each have?

4   Roger and Jackie have 51 cards altogether. Jackie has twice as many cards as Roger. How many do they each have?

5   Charlie and Eddie have 81 crayons altogether. Charlie has half as many crayons as Eddie. How many do they each have?

6   Lisa has twice as many marbles as Bob. Lisa has 30 marbles. How many does Bob have? How many do they have altogether?

7   Boris and Mo have 114 seeds altogether. Mo has 20 more seeds than Boris. How many do they each have?

8   Cherry, Ben and Ilesh have 205 pebbles altogether. Ben has twice as many pebbles as Cherry. Cherry has half as many as Ilesh. How many do they each have?

Classworks © Classworks Numeracy author team, Nelson Thornes Ltd, 2003

Solving Problems (4)

Outcome

Children will be able to decide when to use different operations to solve problems

Medium-term plan objectives

- Choose appropriate number operations and calculation methods to solve money and 'real life' word problems with one or more steps.
- Explain working.
- Check with inverse operation.

Overview

- Apply addition and subtraction to solve problems.
- Use inverse operations to check.
- Apply multiplication and division to solve problems.
- Choose appropriate methods and operations to solve multi-step problems.

How you could plan this unit

	Stage 1	Stage 2	Stage 3	Stage 4	Stage 5
Content and vocabulary	Missing-change problems *inverse, add, subtract*	Solving word problems and explaining work *multiply, multiplied, divided, divide, share*			
Notes	Resource page A				

Missing-change problems

Oral/mental starter pp 185–186

Advance Organiser

We are going to find how much change is missing

You will need: resource page A

Whole-class work

- Read the following problem to the children. Encourage them to listen carefully and to picture what is happening in their heads.

- *I go to the shop with 28p. I buy two packs of sweets for a total of 20p. With the money left over I buy a chew for 2p. How much change should I get?*

- Ask the children to think of how to solve the problem. Encourage them to express it in their own words. Write some ideas on the board.

- Encourage them to suggest jottings or diagrams that will help them solve the problem.

- Provide the following example, if necessary.

I go to the shop   Change

(28p) — I spend 20p / −20p → ( ) — I spend 2p / −2p → ( )

- Read another problem to the children.

- *Marty goes to the newsagents. He has a £1 coin. He buys a comic for 45p and gets 35p change. He checks his change and thinks the newsagent has made a mistake. Is he right?*

- Encourage the children to think carefully again about what happens. Encourage them to check by adding 35p and 45p.

- *What is 35p plus 45p? So what does that mean about our problem? How much more money should the newsagent give to Marty?*

- Look for children suggesting that they subtract 80p from £1, and for others suggesting subtracting 45p from £1 to get 55p and subtracting 35p from this to find the missing amount of change.

Independent, paired or group work

- Ask the children to complete resource page A.

Plenary

- Invite the children to explain how they arrived at some of their answers.

- Work through some of the methods with the class.

- *Who thought of a different way? Who can help us check this answer?*

PUPIL PAGE

Name: _____

Solving money problems

Read each problem carefully and check your answer each time.

1 Raoul spent 16p in the shop. He bought two sweets that cost 12p altogether and one more sweet. How much did that sweet cost?

2 Amit took 27p to the car boot sale. He bought four things and had 14p change. How much did he spend altogether?

3 Janey bought a comic for 23p and two more things that cost 16p altogether. She paid with a 50p coin. How much change should she get?

4 Tariq bought five toys at the car boot sale for 90p. One cost 17p. Another cost twice as much. How much did the others cost altogether?

5 Rushanara bought three things at the market. She had £1.21 in total. Two things cost 55p altogether. The other cost 54p. She was given 2p change. Check her change for her – is this the correct amount?

6 Samir spent £2.36 of his pocket money. He had £1.14 change. How much pocket money did he start with?

Solving word problems and explaining work

Advance Organiser

We are going to decide how to find out how many biscuits each dog has and then solve the problem

Oral/mental starter pp 185–186

You will need: linking cubes or counters

Whole-class work

- Read the following problem to the children and ask them to listen carefully and picture it in their heads as they do so.
- *There are five dogs. Each dog has some biscuits. There are 12 biscuits altogether. One dog has twice as many biscuits as each of the others. How many biscuits does each dog have?*
- Encourage the children to express in their own words what is happening. Encourage ideas for solving the problem and write them on the board.
- Write the following diagram on the board if no other appropriate method is suggested. Model using cubes if necessary.

1st dog	2nd dog	3rd dog	4th dog	5th dog	Total
◯	◯	◯	◯	◯◯	12 biscuits
1 share	1 share	1 share	1 share	2 shares	

- Discuss the diagram with the children and ensure they can relate it to the word problem.
- *How do we solve the problem? Who can tell me what we should do next?*
- Encourage the children to work out that there are six shares of biscuits altogether and to divide 12 by 6 to find the value of one share.
- *Four dogs have two biscuits and one dog has four biscuits. How can we check our answer?*
- Check the answer using some suggested methods, then pose the children a more complex one.
- *There are three spotty dogs. Bill has the fewest spots, Ben has one more spot than Bill, and Bob has one more spot than Ben. There are 21 spots altogether. How many spots does each spotty dog have?*

Independent, paired or group work

- Ask for ideas of how to solve the problem. Model, using linking cubes, if appropriate.
- Allow the children, in their pairs, time to discuss how they will go about solving the problem. Allow them to use cubes and encourage them to record their work.
- Some children may want to draw tables, use jottings and so on.

Plenary

- Invite the children to explain how they solved the problem.
- Ask the children to check each other's work and suggest alternative methods and answers.

Solving Problems (5)

Outcome

Children will be able to solve and explain word problems and check their results using known facts

Medium-term plan objectives	
	● Choose appropriate operations and calculation methods to solve money and 'real life' word problems with one or more steps.
	● Explain working.
	● Check using knowledge of sums of odd/even numbers.

Overview	
	● Use knowledge of odd and even numbers.
	● Use known facts to check answers to problems.
	● Explain how you know an answer or check one.
	● Explain methods.

How you could plan this unit

	Stage 1	Stage 2	Stage 3	Stage 4	Stage 5
Content and vocabulary	Solving problems using known facts *odd, even, add, subtract, minus, take away, difference between, how did you work it out? what could we try next?*	Explaining methods of solving problems *right, correct, wrong, mental calculation, jotting, answer, method, sign, operation, symbol, equation, number sentence*			
Notes					

Solving problems using known facts

Advance Organiser

We are going to check an answer to a problem and explain how we knew

Oral/mental starter pp 185–186

Whole-class work

- Ask the children to listen very carefully to the following word problem. They should close their eyes and visualise it carefully. Write the problem on the board for the children to read as well.

- *Robin has a packet of 70 biscuits and a set of plates. He puts 2 biscuits on each of the plates. When he has finished he says, there are still 37 biscuits in the packet. His friend says, you can't have 37 left if you put 2 on each plate, that's impossible! Who is correct? How do you know?*

- If no one suggests using knowledge of odds and evens, ask children a simpler question.

- *Miranda says the answer to 10 take away 7 is 4. Is she correct? How do you know? Did you have to work it out?*

- Point out, if necessary, that an odd number subtracted from an even number always gives an odd number answer. Return to the problem and draw out this answer. Other children may know their bonds to 10 and be able to tell that the number of children in the class must end with a 3.

- Ask the children to tell you other facts they know about additions and subtractions involving odd and even number answers and write them on the board.

Independent, paired or group work

- Ask the children, in pairs or groups, to listen very carefully to the following word problems. They should answer one or more of them. Write the problems on the board for the children to read as well.

- *Charmain has 17p and her mum gives her 18p more. She looks at the money and guesses that she has about 36p. Is she correct? Explain your answer.*

- *Anna has seven stickers. She needs 20 to fill a whole sticker album. Her friend gives her a pack of 12 more and says 'now you can fill your album!' Is her friend correct? Explain how you know.*

- *Lucy had 27 dolls. She gave 14 to her baby brother. 'That's more than half of them!' she said. Was she correct? Explain how you know.*

Plenary

- Invite the children to explain how they solved some of the puzzles.

- *Who used a different way? Can anyone think how else we could solve the problem? Who can tell me the real answer to that problem?*

Explaining methods of solving problems

Oral/mental starter pp 185–186

Advance Organiser

We are going to explain how we solved a problem, so that our partner can solve it as well

---

Whole-class work

- Read the following problem to the children and write it on the board. Ask them to listen carefully and visualise in their heads what is happening.

- *Belinda goes to the sweet shop with 13p. She can't decide whether to buy toffees or chews. Toffees cost 8p and chews cost 7p. 'Before you decide,' says the shopkeeper, 'I only have 2p coins left in the till!' Which sweet can Belinda buy and get the correct amount of change?*

- Ask the children, in pairs, to think about solving the problem, how they could solve it, and then to find an answer.

- Ask the pairs to tell you their answers only. When a pair gives the correct solution, ask them to the front to explain how to solve the problem to the rest of the class.

- Write their method on the board and agree each stage, pointing out any errors or misconceptions.

- Ask for alternative methods.

- Look for explanations that point out clearly that 2p coins can only make even amounts of money; that Belinda has an odd amount of money; that the sweet she buys must cost an odd amount of money in order to be given an even amount of change.

Independent, paired or group work

- Ask the children to work in pairs. Each child reads and solves one of the following problems on their own. They then explain to their partner how to solve that problem.

- *Benji's step-mum wants to buy light bulbs for all the rooms in her new house. Light bulbs come in packs of two. She counts all the lights in the house and they total 15. How many packs of light bulbs should she buy?*

- *Tomas is at a football match. He counts all the people on the playing field and they total 25. He knows there are 11 players from each field on the pitch. How many extra players are there?*

Plenary

- Invite the children to explain each other's problem-solving methods to the rest of the class.

- Encourage the children to suggest different ways of solving the problems.

- Work through checking the answers with the class.

Solving Problems (6)

Outcome

Children will be able to choose and apply appropriate and systematic approaches to problem-solving

Medium-term plan objectives

- Choose appropriate operations and calculation methods to solve money and 'real life' word problems with one or more steps.
- Explain working.
- Check results by approximating.

Overview

- Use mental calculations to solve problems.
- Use approximation to solve and to check calculations.
- Make decisions and explain working.

How you could plan this unit

	Stage 1	Stage 2	Stage 3	Stage 4	Stage 5
Content and vocabulary	Choosing operations to solve problems *inverse, add, plus, sum, total, multiply, share, divide, approximate, exactly*	Systematic approaches to problem solving *What did you do next? What could we try next? table, grid, row, column*			
Notes	Resource page A				

Choosing operations to solve problems

Advance Organiser

We are going to decide what we need to do to solve a problem and then solve it

Oral/mental starter pp 185–186

You will need: resource page A (one per child and one for you)

Whole-class work

- Read the children the following problem and write it on the board. Ask the children to listen very carefully and encourage them to visualise what is happening at each point.

- *Bus tickets cost 90p each for a single journey. A return ticket costs £1.75. Books of eight single tickets cost £6. What's the cheapest way for Beth to buy tickets to get to and from school every day from Monday to Friday?*

- Ask the children to repeat the problem back to you in their own words. Ask for different ideas on how to solve the problem. Write suggestions on the board.

- Establish that to get to and from school each day, Beth either needs a return ticket or two single tickets and that she needs to travel on five days in all.

- Draw up a list of information that is needed as suggested by the children. Encourage estimating as a quick way to begin solving the problem. For example, encourage children to see quickly that £12 will buy two books of tickets, which is 16 tickets altogether, but that five return tickets will be *less than £10*.

- Suggest tabulating the information to show the alternative costs; for example, as shown.

Type	Cost	Cost of 10 tickets	Total	How many tickets
Single	90p	10 × 90p	£9	10
Return	£1.75	5 × £1.75	£8.75	10
Book of 8	£6	2 × £6	£12	16

- *Can anyone think of a way to buy ten tickets a cheaper way?*

- Encourage the children to use combinations of tickets, using a range of operations and methods to find totals. Encourage them to consider buying more than 10 tickets if that works out cheaper.

- Ask the children to explain how they solved the problem. Check the answer with the children.

Independent, paired or group work

- Ask the children to complete resource page A.

Plenary

- Invite the children to explain how they have solved some of the problems.
- *How did you start?*
- If necessary, revise how to use approximation when approaching the problems.

Name: _____

Solving problems

Ben wants to buy 4 books.
How much will that cost altogether?

Jody wants to buy one of Ben's books
from him. He offers him £2 for one book.
Do you think Ben should sell Jody the
book? Explain why.

All books £2.50 each.
£1 off total order if you
buy more than 3 books.

BARGAIN !

Cuddly toys half price!
Bears were £5, now £2.50!
Spotty dogs were £6.50, now just £3.75!
Chicks were £3, now just £1.50!

Sandy thinks there's a mistake on the
sign. Is she correct? Where is the
mistake? Explain how you know.

Celine says that if she buys two bears,
it's the same as buying one and getting
another one for free. Is she correct?
Explain how you know.

Classworks © Classworks Numeracy author team, Nelson Thornes Ltd, 2003

Systematic approaches to problem solving

Advance Organiser

We are going to organise our work clearly and carefully to help us solve a problem

Oral/mental starter pp 185–186

Whole-class work

- Read the following problem to the children. Ask them to close their eyes and visualise what is happening while you do so.

- *Chocolates cost 20p for lemon creams, 10p for toffees and 5p for caramels. Karen organises the chocolates into boxes of four chocolates. What different amounts will the boxes cost to buy?*

- Ask for ideas of how to go about solving the problem. Ensure that the children write down the required information. Emphasise that there can be more than one sort of chocolate in a box.

- Discuss different methods for finding the costs of the boxes. Encourage the children to use multiplication where appropriate.

- Encourage a systematic approach to begin with; for example, using a table as shown.

Numbers of chocolates	Cost of chocolates		
	20p	10p	5p
1	20p	10p	5p
2	40p	20p	10p
3	60p	30p	15p
4	80p	40p	20p

- Encourage the children to discuss how they will proceed with the rest of the problem. Again, encourage them to organise their work carefully. Emphasise that the more clearly they lay out their working, the more easily they will be able to check and explain their work.

Independent, paired or group work

- Ask the children to solve the problem in pairs, recording how they worked out each stage.

Plenary

- Invite the children to explain how they solved the problem.
- *Where did you start? Why?*
- Ask for alternative methods of working.
- *How can we check our method?*
- Ask some children to explain other children's methods from their recording.

Measures (1)

Outcome

Children will be able to recognise and use units of length and to investigate the perimeter of simple shapes

Medium-term plan objectives

- Use, read and write km, m, cm, mm and mile.
- Know and use relationships between units.
- Know one-half, one-quarter, three-quarters, one-tenth of 1 kilometre in metres; 1 metre in centimetres or millimetres.
- Suggest suitable units and equipment to estimate or measure length.
- Record metres and centimetres using decimals, and other measurements using mixed units.
- Convert up to 1000 cm to metres and vice versa.
- Measure/calculate perimeter of rectangles and simple shapes (cm).
- Choose appropriate number operations and calculation methods to solve measurement word problems with one or more steps.
- Explain and record methods.

Overview

- Converting unit fractions of a kilometre and metre into smaller units.
- Decimal notation of length and conversion of centimetres to metres.
- Finding perimeter of rectangles and simple shapes by measurement and calculation.

How you could plan this unit

	Stage 1	Stage 2	Stage 3	Stage 4	Stage 5
Content and vocabulary	Units of length and distance (1) *measure, measurement, size, unit, metric unit, measuring scale, division, length, width, kilometre, metre, centimetre, millimetre*	Units of length and distance (2) *about the same as, approximately, equivalent to*	Converting metres to centimetres and vice versa *digit, units, ones, tens, hundreds, thousands, numeral, exchange, stands for, represents, place, place value*	Perimeter of rectangles and simple shapes *perimeter, edge*	
Notes	Resource page A	Resource page A	Resource page B	Resource page C	

Units of length and distance (1)

Advance Organiser

We are going to change kilometres to metres, and metres to centimetres

Oral/mental starter pp 186–187

You will need: resource page A (enlarged), objects (1 mm, 1 cm and 1 m long/thick)

Whole-class work

- Show the children the objects described above.

- *This is about one millimetre thick. What does 'milli' tell us in this word? What about the 'centi' in centimetre?*

- Revise the fact that there are 100 cm in 1 m and that the 'centi' in centimetre tells us this. Repeat for 1000 mm in 1 m.

- *How far do you think it is to London or Manchester? How could we measure that in metres? Would it take a long time to count each one? What about millimetres?*

- Show the children an enlarged copy of resource page A. Draw a distance conversion grid on the board with the distance to London (or other destination as appropriate) written in to the nearest kilometre.

Hm	Tm	M	Hth	Tth	Th	H	T	U	
3	6	4	0	0	0	0	0	0	mm
	3	6	4	0	0	0	0	0	cm
			3	6	4	0	0	0	m
						3	6	4	km

- *Who can read this number?*

- Discuss the relationship between kilometres and metres. Point out that 'kilo' refers to the kilometre being the same as 1000 metres.

- Ask a child to write the distance in metres on the grid, then repeat for centimetres and millimetres.

- Ask children to describe what they are doing. If necessary, point out that they are *multiplying by 10, 100 or 1000* each time.

Independent, paired or group work

- Ask the children to answer conversion questions in their books; for example, converting 2 kilometres to metres, writing how many millimetres in 2 metres, *8000 millimetres makes how many metres?* and so on.

Plenary

- Ask the children to discuss their work.

- Ask the children to tell you which is greater or less in pairs of measurements in different metric units; for example, *Which is greater, 46 mm or 6 cm? Which is greater, 52 mm or 3 cm? How did you work that out?*

Name: _____

Units of length

1 km ⟷ 1000 m

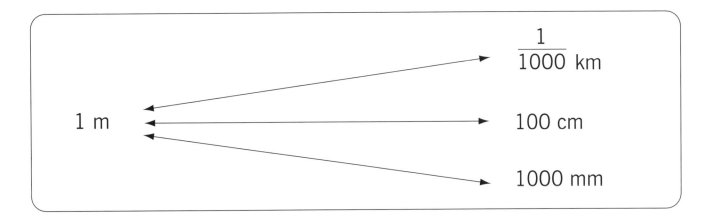

1 m → $\frac{1}{1000}$ km

1 m → 100 cm

1 m → 1000 mm

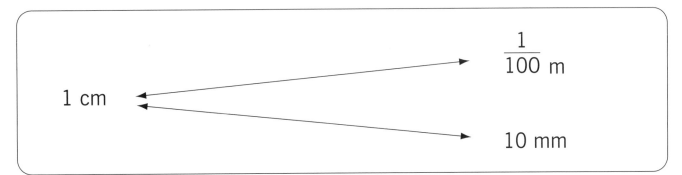

1 cm → $\frac{1}{100}$ m

1 cm → 10 mm

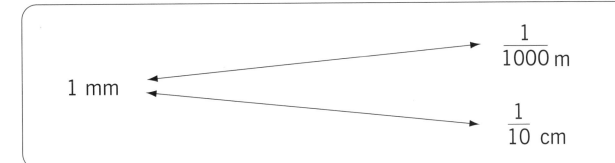

1 mm → $\frac{1}{1000}$ m

1 mm → $\frac{1}{10}$ cm

Units of length and distance (2)

Advance Organiser

We are going to convert parts of larger units of length into smaller units

Oral/mental starter pp 186–187

You will need: resource page A (see page 99) (one per child and one enlarged)

Whole-class work

- Practise conversions between metric units, using resource page A (see page 99) if appropriate.

- *How many metres are there in 5 kilometres? How many centimetres are there in 2 metres?*

- Ask how many centimetres there are in a metre.

- *If there are 100 centimetres in 1 metre, how many centimetres are there in half a metre? How do you know? How did you work it out?*

- *Draw the following diagram on the board.*

- Ensure that the children know what happens in the diagram.

- *This is half a metre, or 50 centimetres. What happens if we extend the diagram? How many centimetres in a quarter of a metre?*

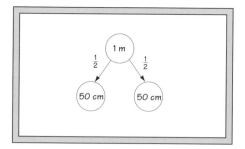

- Continue the diagram as shown.

- *How many metres in 1 kilometre? So how many metres in half a kilometre?*

- Repeat for other 'half' and 'quarter' questions. Refer the children back to resource page A if necessary. Encourage them to see the link between half a metre being 50 cm, and half a kilometre being 500 m.

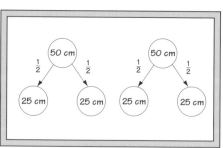

- *How many centimetres in three-quarters of a metre? How did you work that out?*

- Repeat for similar questions, including one-tenth of 1 kilometre in metres, and one-tenth of 1 metre in centimetres.

Independent, paired or group work

- Ask the children to draw 'fraction walls' in their exercise books to show halves, quarters and tenths of kilometres expressed in metres, and of metres expressed in centimetres.

- Early finishers can express these fractions of kilometres in centimetres and attempt expressing these fractions of centimetres in millimetres.

Plenary

- Ask some questions involving mixed units.

- *There are 1000 metres in 1 kilometre. So how many metres in $2\frac{1}{2}$ kilometres?*

- Repeat for centimetres and metres.

Converting metres to centimetres and vice versa

Advance Organiser

We are going to write how many centimetres in 1.6 metres

Oral/mental starter pp 186–187

You will need: resource page B (one per child)

Whole-class work

- Remind the children that there are 100 cm in a metre and that cm can be written as m using a decimal point.

- Write on the board: *1.2 m.*

- *What have I written? Who can tell me what it means?*

- Remind the children that this is read as *one point two metres.*

- *How many centimetres in 1.2 metres? How do you know?*

- If necessary, write a place-value table on the board. Write 1.2 m and 120 cm in the appropriate place as shown.

- Write on the board: *250 cm.*

- Who can tell me what this means? How many metres are there? How could we write that?

H	T	U	•	t	
		1	•	2	m
1	2	0	•	0	cm

- Discuss writing this as *2.5 m* with reference to place value again.

- Repeat for other metre and centimetre conversions, including 0.6 m and 75 cm if appropriate.

Independent, paired or group work

- Ask the children to complete resource page B.

- Early finishers can measure items in the classroom and write the measurements in metres and in centimetres.

Plenary

- Ask some quick questions converting fractions of measures to decimals and vice versa.

- *How many centimetres in $2\frac{1}{2}$ metres? This table is 125 centimetres long. How many meters is that? How could we write that another way?*

Name: _____

Metres and centimetres

Write these measurements as metres.

260 cm ....

990 cm ....

470 cm ....

82 cm ....

800 cm ....

450 cm ....

Write these measurements as centimetres.

6·2 m ....

0·8 m ....

1·8 m ....

18·2 m ....

9·1 m ....

25·5 m ....

Perimeter of rectangles and simple shapes

Advance Organiser

We are going to measure the perimeters of some shapes

Oral/mental starter
pp 186–187

You will need: square, resource page C (one per child and one enlarged), Blu-Tack, pipe-cleaners

Whole-class work

- Show the children a square and stick it to the board with Blu-Tack.
- *Each side of this square is 10 cm long. Imagine a spider walking all the way around the sides of this square. How far would it have walked altogether?*
- Ask the children for ideas of how to solve the problem. Write suggestions on the board.
- Encourage them to see that the distance will be the same as all the lengths of the sides added together.
- If necessary, demonstrate using pipe-cleaners, opening a square or rectangle out for the children to see.
- Ask the children if they know what *perimeter* means. Write it on the board.
- Introduce perimeter as being the distance all around a shape.
- Show the children an enlarged copy of resource page C.
- Model measuring the sides of the first rectangle on squared paper, describing what you are doing at each stage.
- Encourage the children to look at the measurements and add them together. Some of them will want to count the squares as they go around the shape – this is acceptable at this stage.
- *Who can see a short cut? How do you know that is correct?*
- Encourage the use of doubling to aid calculation, writing it on the board as shown.
- Rub two of the measurements off the board. *How can I work out the perimeter now?*
- Encourage the children to double each measurement then add them together.
- Try for more rectangles with only two measurements given.

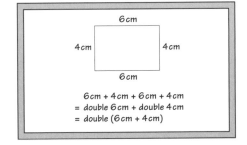

6 cm + 4 cm + 6 cm + 4 cm
= double 6 cm + double 4 cm
= double (6 cm + 4 cm)

Independent, paired or group work

- Ask the children to complete resource page C. Children will find it harder moving to rectangles not on squared paper.

Plenary

- Look at the shapes in questions 1 to 3.
- *Can anyone see a quick way of working these out?*
- Encourage the children to explain how they did this.
- Look at the shapes in questions 6 and 7.
- *Were you able to work out the lengths of the unmarked sides? How?*

Name: _____

Perimeter

Find the perimeter of each rectangle.

1 4 cm / 2 cm / 4 cm / 2 cm

2 3 cm / 2 cm / 4 cm / 3 cm

3 6 cm / 5 cm / 4 cm / 5 cm / 6 cm

4 22 cm / 11 cm / 11 cm / 22 cm

5 100 cm / 60 cm / 60 cm / 100 cm

6 9 m / 6 m

7 7 m / 7 m

Classworks © Classworks Numeracy author team, Nelson Thornes Ltd, 2003

Measures (2)

Outcome

Children will be able to read and record time, and calculate time intervals

Medium-term plan objectives	• Use, read and write vocabulary of time. • Read time to 1 minute on analogue/12-hour digital clock. • Use 9:53, am and pm. • Solve time word problems.
Overview	• Read and record time to 1 minute. • Use am and pm. • Calculate time intervals. • Solve time word problems.

How you could plan this unit

	Stage 1	Stage 2	Stage 3	Stage 4	Stage 5
Content and vocabulary	Time to the minute *time, hour, minute, second, o'clock, half past, quarter to, quarter past, clock, watch, hands, digital, analogue, takes longer, takes less time*	Problems with time *how long will it take to?, am, pm, noon, takes longer, takes less time*			
Notes	Resource page A	Resource page B			

Time to the minute

Advance Organiser

We are going to read and record time accurately on analogue and digital clocks

Oral/mental starter pp 186–187

You will need: geared analogue clock face with numerals 1 to 12, minutes marked and labelled in fives, digital clock face, resource page A (one per child)

Whole-class work

- Show the children the analogue clock face.

- *Who can help me read the time? Which hand shows us the hours? Which shows us the minutes?*

- Set the analogue clock to 6 minutes past the hour and ask what time it is.

- Point out that the minute hand is *1 minute beyond* the number 1 on the dial that indicates 5 minutes past.

- *So 1 minute more than 5 minutes is 6 minutes past.*

- Move the minute finger around to a minute before quarter past, then 1 and then 2 minutes after quarter past, asking how many minutes past each time.

- Continue moving around the dial, positioning the minute finger 1, 2 or 3 minutes before and after each multiple of 5 minutes.

- Ask the children to explain how they are reading the time. Ensure that counting in fives is mentioned, then adjusting according to the precise position of the minute hand.

- Draw on the board a clock face with markings and numbers but no hands.

- Point to various positions and ask the children to read how many minutes each time.

- Remind them that just before or past a multiple of 5 is 1 minute before or after, just before or after halfway is 2 minutes before or after.

- Show the children the digital clock face.

- *Who can tell me what time this shows?*

- Encourage the children to read the times in different ways; for example, *5:13* can be read as *five thirteen, thirteen minutes past five, nearly a quarter past five,* and so on.

Independent, paired or group work

- Ask the children to complete resource page A, matching the digital to analogue clock times.

Plenary

- Ask the children to come to the front of the class to move the analogue clock to match digital times on resource page A.

- Ask the rest of the children to say if they agree, and why.

- Invite the children to write their own digital times on the board, and ask them to read the times out in different forms of words.

Name: _____

Digital and analogue

Match the pairs of clocks that say the same time.

5:24

4:38

11:41

2:03

10:10

Problems with time

Oral/mental starter
pp 186–187

Advance Organiser

We are going to solve some time problems

You will need: resource page B (one per child)

Whole-class work

- Ask the children if they can tell you the meaning of *am* and *pm*.

- Explain, or correct as necessary, that they mean respectively *before* and *after* the *middle of the day*.

- Explain why the *m* stands for *meridian*, the middle of the day (from the Latin *meridies)*, the *a* stands for *ante* (*before*) and the *p* for *post* (*after*).

- Reinforce the children's understanding by asking a few paired questions, such as *What will you be doing today at 1 pm? What were you doing today at 1 am?*

- *How long is it between 9:30 am and 10:20 am?*

- This can be worked out mentally because 10:30 would be one hour later than 9:30, so this answer must be 10 minutes less than an hour.

- *How long is it between 10:48 am and 11:37 am?*

- This problem is much harder to solve mentally. Again, ask children to discuss how to solve the problem. Draw the following diagram on the board to illustrate the problem. Ask the children to describe to you how it can be used to help.

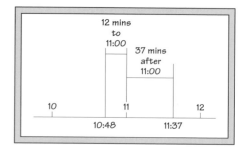

- Add the two 'jumps' or sections of time together, ensuring that the children know what you are doing and why.

- *John leaves home at 8:15. He gets the bus to school with his friends and then plays for a while. The bell goes just before 9:00 and he sits down for the register at 9:10. How long since he left home?*

Independent, paired or group work

- Ask the children to solve the problems on resource page B.

Plenary

- Discuss the children's answers and methods to resource page B.

- Ask the children to suggest word problems based on their own school day. Work through examples with the class.

Name: _____

Solving time problems

Read each question carefully and solve the problem.

1 Corey finishes assembly at 9:15 am and does some quiet reading. He starts maths at nine-forty am. How long did he read for?

2 Sally worked hard from five past eleven in the morning until 12:30 pm. How long was she working?

3 In the evening, Paulo played on his console from 6:25 until 8:58. He was only supposed to play for an hour at most. Did he play for longer or shorter than an hour?

4 Copy and complete these sentences:

(a) I go to bed at ………. pm and get up at ………. am. Altogether I spend ………. hours and ………. minutes in bed.

(b) I arrive at school at ………. am and go home at ………. pm. Altogether I spend ………. hours ………. minutes in school.

Measures (3)

Outcome

Children will be able to measure and solve problems involving measures

Medium-term plan objectives

- Estimate and check times using seconds, minutes and hours.
- Measure and compare using kilograms and grams, and know and use the relationship between them.
- Know one-quarter, one-half, three-quarters and one-tenth of 1 kilogram in grams.
- Suggest suitable units and equipment to estimate or measure mass.
- Read scales.
- Record measurements to suitable degree of accuracy, using mixed units, or the nearest whole/half/quarter unit (for example, 3.25 kg).
- Measure and calculate area of rectangles and simple shapes, using counting methods and standard units (square centimetres).
- Choose appropriate number operations and calculation methods to solve measurement word problems with one or more steps.
- Explain working.

Overview

- Estimate time, choosing units of time.
- Revise kilograms and grams.
- Measure area.
- Solve problems involving measures.

How you could plan this unit

	Stage 1	Stage 2	Stage 3	Stage 4	Stage 5
Content and vocabulary	Hours, minutes and seconds *hour, minute, second, takes longer, takes less time, how long will it take to?*	Kilograms and grams *balance, scales, kilogram, half kilogram, gram*	Measuring area *area, covers, surface, square centimetre (cm²)*	Problems involving mass *what could we try next?, how did you work it out?, calculate, method, jotting, answer, right, correct, wrong, number sentence*	
			Resource page A	Resource page B	
Notes					

110

Hours, minutes and seconds

Advance Organiser

We are going to look at how we use different units of time

You will need: stopwatches, class clock

Whole-class work

- Write on the board in a column: *1 hour*, *1 minute* and *1 second*.

- *What can you tell me about 1 hour? What could you do in 1 hour? How many minutes in 1 hour?*

- Build up the following diagram on the board with the help of the children.

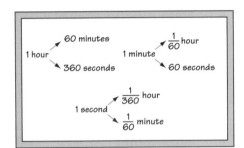

- Talk about which units would be best for timing a variety of events: school day, playtime, time spent watching TV in a day, reciting 2 times-table and so on.

- Ask the children to estimate, for example, how long it would take to walk all around the playground. Encourage them to refer to benchmarks.

- *Lauren, our maths lesson lasts just less than 1 hour. Would it take you that long to walk around the playground? Would it take a bit less, or much less time?*

- *Riham, it takes you about 15 minutes to eat breakfast. Would it take you that long to walk around the playground? A bit less?*

- Ask the children to help you build up a list of actions that take: *more than 1 hour, less than 1 hour*; *more than 1 minute, less than 1 minute*; and *more than 1 second, less than 1 second*. If they suggest, for example, adding *travelling to Leeds* to the table for *more than 1 second*, discuss whether this is *much more* or *just a bit more* than 1 second. How would they measure the time it took most easily?

Independent, paired or group work

- Ask the children to estimate five things that they can do until the end of the lesson and write them down. Encourage them to write an estimate of how long each will take.

- Allow them to adjust their first estimate of the overall time in the light of their other estimates. Once they have made all their estimates, ask them to carry out the tasks in pairs, timing each other and recording their times.

Plenary

- Discuss the children's estimates and timings, and compare them.

- Ask if anyone had put down any *interesting* or *imaginative* events to time.

- *Who was surprised by how long something took?*

Kilograms and grams

Advance Organiser

We are going to convert grams to kilograms and kilograms to grams

Oral/mental starter pp 186–187

You will need: balances, scales

Whole-class work

- Consolidate knowledge that 1 kg is the same as 1000 g. Ask a few quick questions.

- *How many grams are there in half a kilogram?*

- Make sure that everyone understand that *kg* and *g* are abbreviations for *kilogram* and *gram*, and that we often shorten *kilogram* to *kilo*. Explain that *kilo* means *one thousand*.

- *How many grams are there in three-quarters of a kilogram?*

- Work through the children's suggestions, guiding them towards identifying that there are 1000 grams in 1 kilogram, then build up the following diagram to show the relationship on the board.

- *So, how many grams are there in one-quarter of a kilogram? What about in half a kilogram? How do you know?*

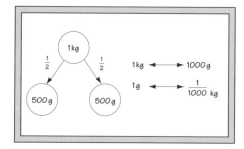

Independent, paired or group work

- Ask the children to complete the following conversions of grams to kilograms and vice versa.

- $\frac{5}{10}$ of a kilogram is the same as .... g; $\frac{1}{10}$ of a kilogram is the same as ....g; 500 grams is the same as ..... of a kilogram; $\frac{1}{4}$ of a kilogram is the same as ..... grams; $\frac{3}{4}$ kg is the same as ..... g; 800 g is the same as ..... of a kilogram; $\frac{1}{4}$ kg is the same as .... g; 1500 grams is the same as .... kg.

Plenary

- Ask the children to explain some of the conversions and answers for the above questions.

- Ask some quick questions to finish.

- *How many grams are there in $\frac{7}{10}$ of a kilogram? How many grams are there in $\frac{3}{10}$ of a kilogram? What fraction of a kilogram is 600g? How many grams are there in $3\frac{1}{2}$ kg? How many grams are there in $2\frac{3}{4}$ kg? How many grams are there in $\frac{9}{10}$ of a kilogram? How many grams are there in $8\frac{1}{2}$ kg?*

Measuring area

Advance Organiser

We are going to measure the area of a square

**Oral/mental starter
pp 186–187**

You will need: centimetre-squared paper, rectangles measuring an exact number of
centimetres in each dimension (per group), Centicubes, resource page A

Whole-class work

- Give each group of children a small rectangle. Ask them to tell you about its properties. Ask them to look at its flat surface.
- *How many centimetre cubes could cover the surface of this rectangle leaving no space?*
- Ask the children to estimate (make a 'good guess') and then check in their groups.
- Emphasise that they have to cover the shape *completely* with squared paper.
- Introduce the term *area* and write it on the board.
- *How many centimetre cubes covered your rectangle?*
- Write on the board: *14 cm cubes.* Then after it: *14 square centimetres.*
- *Who can tell me what this means?*
- Show the children the diagram of a square centimetre blown up on resource page A (also shown here).

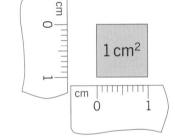

- Point out that it measures 1 cm in both directions – it is square. Explain that we can use the sign ^{2} to mean 'squared' and that it suggests *2 directions of measurement*.
- Explain that we can use square centimetres to measure flat space.
- Show the children the first question on resource page A and indicate the square centimetres marked on it.
- *How may squares does this rectangle take up?*
- *There are 3 rows of 2, or turned around this way, 2 rows of 3. How many altogether?*
- If no one has volunteered that you can avoid counting by using multiplication, point it out.
- Use calculation to work out the area of another rectangle on resource page A.
- Work out one of the last three questions, explaining that the children can either count the squares, or multiply and 'take away' the missing squares.

Independent, paired or group work

- Ask the children to complete resource page A. The last problems will challenge early finishers.

Plenary

- Discuss any difficulties, then go through the last two questions asking the children to help you solve them.
- How did the children (who got the right answer) work it out? Did they subtract the missing area, split the shape up into rectangular sections, or simply add up the squares?

Name: _____

Measuring area

Find the area of each rectangle.

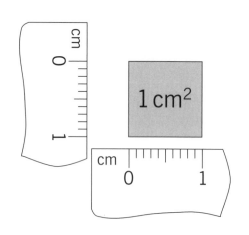

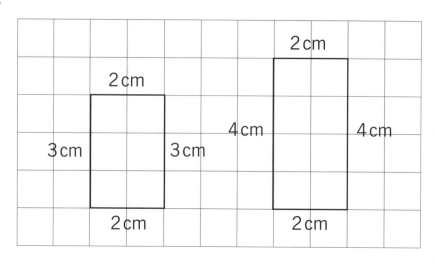

Find the area of each rectangle by calculating. They are not drawn to scale.

7 cm
3 cm

4 cm
4 cm

8 cm
5 cm

Write the area of each shape. Say how you worked out the answer.

4 cm
4 cm

4 cm
5 cm

3 cm
5 cm

Problems involving mass

Advance Organiser

We are going to solve problems by breaking them down into stages

Oral/mental starter
p 186–187

You will need: resource page B

Whole-class work

- Revise units of mass with the children, ensuring that they know there are 1000 grams in 1 kilogram.

- Try a few quick mass questions; for example, *400 grams take away 200 grams makes what? How many lots of 25 grams in 100 grams? How did you work that out?*

- Write on the board, and read to the children, the following problem.

- *A builder needs 15 kg of cement for one mixer full of concrete. If he has five 25 kg bags of cement, how many lots of concrete can he mix? How much cement does he have left over?*

- Encourage the children to picture this in their head and follow the actions. What is happening in the problem? Is something being added together, or shared out, or made larger or smaller?

- Ask the children to say in their own words what has happened.

- Discuss how the answer can be worked out by breaking it down into stages, based on what we know, what we need to find out, and how we find it out.

- *How many kilograms of cement does he have altogether? How do we work that out? (5 × 25 kg = 125 kg) What do we need to find out next? (125 kg grouped in lots of 15 kg) How do we work that out?*

- Work through the stages with the children, taking ideas for different ways of working at each stage.

- Use the board to do the necessary computation with the children.

- Re-work the problems with different numbers, if necessary.

Independent, paired or group work

- Ask the children to complete resource page B, pointing out that they should show how they arrived at their answer.

- Ask them to read the questions very carefully.

Plenary

- Select two or three of the problems and ask the children how they worked out their (correct) answer.

- Identify a problem that most/all the children found difficult.

- *What do we know?*

- *What do we need to know to find the answer?*

- *How do we find out what we need to know?*

- Work out the problem together, using the board to show how.

Name: _____

Solving mass problems

Answer these questions and write down **how** you found the answer.

1 60 grams add 230 grams makes ....

2 Half of 1.5 kg makes how many grams? ....

3 If you need 140 g of butter to bake 30 biscuits, what you would need to bake 60 biscuits? ....

4 12 pencils and a pencil sharper weigh 98 g together. The sharpener weighs 14 g. How heavy is one pencil? ....

5 How many 4 kg bags of sweets are needed to give 30 children 250 g of sweets each? ....

6 Andy eats 150 g of chocolate a day. How many days will a 1.2 kg block last? ....

Classworks © Classworks Numeracy author team, Nelson Thornes Ltd, 2003

Measures (4)

Outcome

Children will be able to read and measure capacity, and solve problems involving capacity

Medium-term plan objectives	• Use, read, write: litre (l), millilitre (ml), pint.
	• Know one-quarter, one-half, three-quarters and one-tenth of 1 litre in ml.
	• Suggest suitable units and equipment to estimate or measure capacity.
	• Read scales.
	• Record measurements to suitable degree of accuracy, using mixed units, or the nearest whole/half/quarter unit (for example, 3.25 litres).
	• Choose appropriate number operations and calculation methods to solve measurement word problems with one or more steps.
	• Explain working.
Overview	• Look at units of capacity.
	• Read scales on the measuring containers.
	• Record litres and parts of litres in decimal notation.
	• Solve problems related to capacity.

How you could plan this unit

	Stage 1	Stage 2	Stage 3	Stage 4	Stage 5
Content and vocabulary	Capacity in litres, millilitres and pints capacity, full, half-full, empty, holds, contains, litre, half-litre, millilitre, pint, container, measuring cylinder	Reading scales measuring scale, division, guess, estimate, nearly, roughly, about, close to	Recording capacity in litres, using decimals units, ones, tens, hundreds, thousands, ten thousand, hundred thousand, million, digit, numeral, place, place value	Word problems involving capacity what could we try next?, how did you work it out?, method, jotting, answer, right, correct, wrong	
Notes		Resource page A		Resource page B	

Capacity in litres, millilitres and pints

Advance Organiser

We are going to compare capacity in litres, millilitres and pints

Oral/mental starter pp 186–187

You will need: litre measure, pint bottle or carton

Whole-class work

- Show the children a litre measure, and write on the board: *1 litre.*
- *What do we measure in litres? Who can tell me how many millilitres are in one litre?*
- Consolidate knowledge that 1 litre is the same as 1000 ml.
- Ask a few quick questions, such as: *How many millilitres are there in half a litre?*
- Make sure everyone understand that *l* and *ml* are abbreviations for *litre* and *millilitre.*
- Ask more questions, building up the following diagram on the board, including quarters of a litre.
- Ask some questions not pertaining to the diagram.

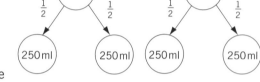

- *How many millilitres are there in one-tenth of a litre? How can we work that out?*
- Display a place-value chart if necessary.
- *So, how many millilitres are there in two-tenths of a litre? What about in three-tenths of a litre?*
- Show the children a pint measure next to the litre measure.
- *Who can tell me what this is? Who has heard of the word 'pint'?*
- Write on the board: *pint.*
- Discuss the fact that people still use pints to measure capacity.
- Remind the children that the pint is not a metric measure so it doesn't easily convert.
- Use a pint milk bottle to fill up a litre measure, demonstrating that 1 pint is just more than half a litre, and 1 litre is just less than 2 pints.
- Ask some quick questions about pints and litres.
- *About how many pints are there in 1 litre? About how many pints in 2 litres?*

Independent, paired or group work

- Ask the children to answer some conversion questions; for example, $\frac{1}{10}$ of a litre is the same as ☐ millilitres; $\frac{1}{4}$ of a litre is the same as ☐ ml; 500 millilitres is the same as ☐ of a litre; 4 pints is a little more than ☐ litres, and so on.

Plenary

- Go through some of the questions with the class.
- Ask the class which they think is more, 6 pints or 4 litres. Demonstrate with a measuring cylinder and the pint and litre measures. Repeat for similar comparisons.

Reading scales

Advance Organiser

We are going to look at different scales used in measuring capacity

Oral/mental starter pp 186–187

You will need: measuring cylinders and jugs, dipstick (pencil or similar), resource page A (one per child)

Whole-class work

- Look at a collection of measuring containers and the scales on them.

- *Who can tell me something about this measuring container? What is the largest capacity it could measure? How do you know?*

- Sketch on the board one of the scales, complete with numbers and divisions.

- Point to an unnumbered mark and ask the children to read the capacity.

- *How did you work that out?*

- Point to the scale halfway between two of the marks.

- *How could you estimate what this reading means?*

- Repeat for further levels one-quarter of the way or three-quarters of the way between marks. Encourage children to find the amount of millilitres covered by the two marks either side, and to perform the appropriate calculation.

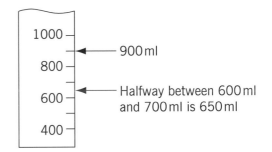

- Talk through the principle of a dipstick.

- Use an improvised dipstick (such as a pencil) to demonstrate how to read one.

- Emphasise the importance of keeping it vertical.

Independent, paired or group work

- Ask the children to complete resource page A.

- Discuss the farmer' problem. Point out that, for example, in order to find how much oil he used in October, they need to work out the difference between the readings taken on 1st October and 1st November.

Plenary

- Check a few of the intermediate readings with the class.

- Discuss the word problem with the children and ask how they solved it.

- Write ideas on the board and work through them, checking some of the answers with the class.

Name: _____

Reading scales

Look at these measuring containers. What do the readings show?

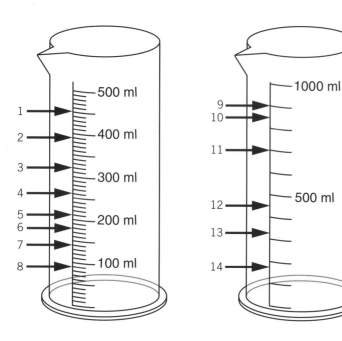

A farmer uses an oil boiler to heat his cowsheds.
At the start of each month he uses a dipstick to see how much oil is left in his tank.

Approximately how much oil did he use in
21 October?
22 November?
23 December?
24 January?
25 Which was the coldest month?
26 Why do you think that?
27 Which was the warmest month?
28 Why do you think that?

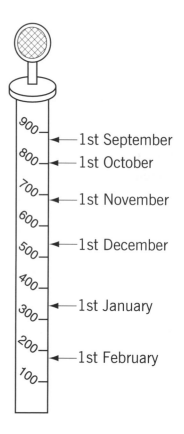

Classworks © Classworks Numeracy author team, Nelson Thornes Ltd, 2003

Recording capacity in litres, using decimals

Oral/mental starter
pp 186–187

Advance Organiser

We are going to write down capacities in litres, using decimals instead of millilitres

You will need: measuring cylinders/jugs

Whole-class work

- Write down a few measures on the left-hand side of the board, using mixed units (such as 2 litres 300 millilitres).

- Remind the children that a decimal point can be used to separate whole numbers from parts of whole numbers (tenths, hundredths, thousandths and so on).

- *Because millilitres are parts of a litre they can be written as a decimal.*

- Ask some children to approach the board to rewrite each measurement on the right-hand side using decimal notation and just the *l* symbol.

- Ask other children to read out the measurements.

- Encourage children to use language such as *two point two-five millilitres* and *two litres two hundred and fifty millilitres* and also *two and a quarter millilitres.*

- Point out that one-tenth of a litre is shown by a *1* in the tenths column, two-tenths by a *2* and so on.

- Remind them that zeros that do not come between numerals, or between numerals and the decimal point, can be omitted.

- Show them a place-value conversion chart if necessary.

Th	H	T	U	•	t	
			4	•	2	l
4	2	0	0	•	0	ml

Independent, paired or group work

- Ask the children to rewrite some more measurements in litre form using a decimal point and omitting unnecessary zeroes.

- For example, *3 litres 250 ml, 1 litre 125 ml, 2 litres 310 ml, 4 litres 500 ml, 1 litre 150 ml, 3 litres 800 ml, 2 litres 57 ml, 3 litres 0 ml, 0 litres 250 ml, 2 litres 50 ml.*

- Then ask them to copy these measurements and change the fractions into decimals:
$3\frac{1}{4}$ *l*, $2\frac{3}{10}$ *l*, $4\frac{1}{2}$ *l* and so on.

Plenary

- Demonstrate measuring some amounts of water and asking the children to read the levels.

- Ask other children to say the levels in a different form, using fractions, litres and millilitres, or decimals.

- Write the equivalent capacities on the board and ensure all the children agree.

Word problems involving capacity

Advance Organiser

We are going to solve word problems in stages

Oral/mental starter pp 186–187

You will need: resource page B

Whole-class work

- Practise a few quick calculations involving litres. Remind the children there are 1000 millilitres in 1 litre.

- *What is half of 2 litres? What is 1.3 litres plus 400 millilitres? How did you work that out? What is 2.5 litres take away half a litre?*

- Write the following problem on the board and read it aloud to the children. Encourage them to close their eyes and picture in their heads what is happening.

- *A painter needs 2 litres of paint to cover the walls of a room in one coat. He needs to put on two coats of paint. How many 2.5 litre tins of paint does he need to buy to paint the whole room? How much paint does he have left over?*

- Discuss how the problem can be worked out by breaking it down into stages.

- Encourage the children to think about what they know already, what they need to find out and how they can work out that information.

- *How much paint is needed altogether? How do we work that out? How much is in each tin? So how many tins does he need to buy to have equal to or greater than 4 litres of paint? How much do these two tins hold? So how much paint will be left over?*

- Ask the children to explain different stages of the calculation. Work through it, adding the amounts of paint for each coat, working out that they need to buy more tins than they need as the paint is available only in 2.5 litre tins, and so on.

- Check the answer using different methods, such as equivalent calculations or inverse operations.

- Repeat with a different problem, or with different data.

Independent, paired or group work

- Ask the children to complete the problems on resource page B.

- Point out that they need to write two problems of their own and to swap them with a partner, so that questions 9 and 10 that they answer are a partner's questions.

Plenary

- Look at some of the problems on the sheet and go through the stages required to solve them quickly.

- Work through one or two of the best problems that the children wrote. Ask them to explain how they solved it. Ask the children who set them to explain how they decided to write their problem in that way.

Name: _____

Problems using capacity

1 A car uses 4 litres of petrol to travel 30 miles. How much petrol does it need to travel 150 miles?

2 The school kitchen puts 150 ml of custard on each portion of apple pie. How much custard is needed for 100 portions?

3 A scoop of ice cream is 50 ml. How many scoops could be served from a 4 litre tub?

4 **(a)** How many 3 litre bottles of pop are needed to give 30 children a 250 ml drink?
(b) How much pop would be left over?

5 The paddling pool could hold 250 litres of water. How many 10 litre buckets of water are needed to half fill it?

6 The instructions on a bottle of weedkiller tell you to add 25 ml to a litre of water. How much water would a gardener need to mix with the whole 200 ml bottle?

7 Mum is planting sunflower seeds in $2\frac{1}{2}$ litre plant pots.
(a) How much potting compost does she need for 20 pots?
(b) How many 40 litre bags of compost will she need to buy?
(c) How much compost will she have left over?

8 Alison and Rachel both need to take a 5 ml spoon of cough medicine three times a day. How many days will a 120 ml bottle last?

9 and 10 Make up two problems of your own and exchange them with a partner. See who can solve the other's problems first.

Classworks © Classworks Numeracy author team, Nelson Thornes Ltd, 2003

Measures (5)

Outcome

Children will be able to use a calendar, interpret timetables and solve problems related to time

Medium-term plan objectives

- Read timetables and use this year's calendar.
- Solve problems involving time.

Overview

- Use this year's calendar.
- Extract information from a timetable.
- Solve problems.

How you could plan this unit

	Stage 1	Stage 2	Stage 3	Stage 4	Stage 5
Content and vocabulary	This year's calendar *Monday, Tuesday and so on; January, February and so on; day, week, fortnight, month, spring, summer, autumn, winter, year, leap year, weekend, birthday, holiday, calendar, date, date of birth*	Timetables *quick, quicker, quickest, early, late, earlier, later, earliest, latest, fast, faster, fastest, slow, slower, slowest, takes longer, takes less time, how long will it be to?, timetable, arrive, depart, hour, minute, second*			
Notes	Resource page A	Resource page B			

This year's calendar

Advance Organiser

We are going to look at this year's calendar and answer some questions

Oral/mental starter pp 186–187

You will need: copies of this year's calendar, as many different ones as possible, resource page A (one per child)

Whole-class work

- Look at the different ways calendars are laid out – on a sheet, on 12 pages, with days numbered in columns or rows, weeks beginning on Sunday or Monday.

- Look at how weekend days are sometimes coloured differently from weekdays.

- *Why do you think these days are sometimes represented differently? What is different about these days?*

M	T	W	Th	F	S	S
			1	2	3	4
5	6	7	8	9	10	11
12	13	14	15	16	17	18

- Practise some questions with the children.

- *List the months in order, starting with January.*

- *List the days that each month starts on.*

- *How many days are there in February this year?*

- *Which months have five Sundays?*

- *Which months have only four Sundays?*

- *What day of the week is Christmas Day on this year? Who can tell me any special dates? When is Diwali? When will you be celebrating New Year? Who can tell me when their birthday is?*

Independent, paired or group work

- Ask the children to use a copy of this year's calendar to answer the questions on resource page A.

- Children who finish can compare this year's calendar with last year's, or next year's calendar.

Plenary

- Look at questions 2 and 3.

- If no one has noticed, point out that months without an *r* are generally warmer months. In the days before refrigeration some foods were only eaten if there *was* an *r* in the month, meaning that it was cooler and that the food kept better.

- If some children got on to comparing this year with last year, did they notice anything? For example, months tending to start one or two days later than they started in the previous year.

- *How many days are there this year? What is that in weeks and days?*

Name: _____

This year's calendar

Look at this year's calendar and answer these questions.

1 What day will next year begin on?

2 Which month names do not contain a letter r?

3 What do you notice about the months that do not have a letter r?

4 Write the date of the second Monday in April, in words and in numbers.

5 Using just numbers, write the dates of the Thursdays in September.

6 How many days are there from 1st January to 31st March?

7 How many weeks are there between 1st March and 1st November?

8 How many weeks and days is it until the start of the summer holidays?

9 How many weeks and days are there in this term?

10 What was the date of Easter Sunday this year?

11 What day and date comes exactly 12 weeks before 16th May?

12 Which date comes next, your birthday, November 5th, or Christmas Day?

Classworks © Classworks Numeracy author team, Nelson Thornes Ltd, 2003

Timetables

Advance Organiser

We are going to solve some time problems with a train timetable

Oral/mental starter pp 186–187

You will need: resource page B (per child and one enlarged)

Whole-class work

- Look at the display version of the railway timetable on resource page B.

- Discuss the meaning of terms such as *arrival* and *departure*.

- Ask the children to answer some quick questions identifying parts of the timetable.

- *What time is the earliest departure from Birmingham? When does the next train leave Birmingham? If I want to leave Birmingham after 8.00, which train should I take?*

- Work through some calculations of time intervals. Encourage the children to picture a number line and count on over hour boundaries, remembering that there are 60 minutes in 1 hour.

- For example, *How many minutes between 6.48 am and 7.34 am?*

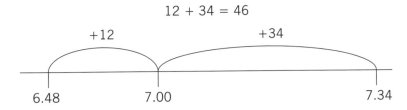

- *From 6.48 until 7.00 is 12 minutes. Then add 34 minutes more, which makes 46 minutes altogether.*

- Repeat for some examples across hour boundaries and across noon or midnight.

Independent, paired or group work

- Ask the children to complete resource page B.

Plenary

- Ask the children to explain how they solved some of the problems.

- Discuss the variations in the times of the trains. (This section of timetable is based on a real train timetable.)

- *Why might some parts of journeys take longer?* (Answers could include fitting in with other train movements on the tracks, some trains stopping at more stations along the route and so on.)

- *Which trains are likely to be the busiest? Why?*

Name: _____

Train timetables

Here is part of a train timetable.

Birmingham (departure)	5:40	6:15	6:48	7:14	07:44	08:10
Warwick (departure)	6:11	6:47	7:23	7:47	08:18	08:47
Banbury (departure)	6:32	7:06	7:45	8:07	08:42	09:09
London (arrival)	7:51	8:25	9:15	9:28	10:01	10:35

1 How long does the 5.40 from Birmingham take until it leaves Warwick?

2 The 6.15 train leaves Birmingham. How long until it leaves Warwick?

3 How long does it take for the 7.47 from Warwick to get to London?

4 If you wanted to arrive in London by 9 o'clock, what is the latest time you could leave Banbury?

5 What other times could you leave Banbury to get to London in time?

6 If you wanted to arrive in London before 10 o'clock, what is the latest time you could leave Warwick?

7 If you got to Banbury station at 7:20, how long would you wait for a train to leave? What time should it arrive in London?

8 If you got to Birmingham station at 7:50, how long would you wait for a train to leave? What time should it arrive in London?

9 Which train is the quickest from Birmingham to London?

10 Which train is the slowest from Birmingham to London?

Shape and Space (1)

Outcome

Children will be able to use a variety of criteria for sorting shapes, find points on a numbered grid and explore a general statement about shapes

Medium-term plan objectives	
	• Describe and visualise 3-D and 2-D shapes, including tetrahedron and heptagon.
	• Recognise equilateral and isosceles triangles.
	• Classify shapes (right angles, regularity, symmetry).
	• Recognise positions on grids with numbered lines.
	• Investigate general statements about shapes.

Overview	
	• Classify 3-D shapes.
	• Recognise equilateral and isosceles triangles.
	• Use grids with numbered lines to find and join points.
	• Investigate the statement that 'If you join the midpoints of any triangle you get four smaller, equal triangles'.

How you could plan this unit

	Stage 1	Stage 2	Stage 3	Stage 4	Stage 5
Content and vocabulary	Sorting and classifying 2-D and 3-D shapes

polyhedron, regular, irregular face, square-based pyramid, tetrahedron, cube, octahedron, triangular, 3D, three-dimensional | Recognising equilateral and isosceles triangles

triangle, isosceles, equilateral, angle, equal, scalene, side, vertices | Using grids with numbered lines

coordinates, grid, x-axis, y-axis, horizontal, vertical, line | Investigating general statements about shapes

midpoint, general statement, accuracy, equilateral triangle, isoceles triangle | |
| **Notes** | | | Resource page A | Resource page B | |

129

Sorting and classifying 2-D and 3-D shapes

Oral/mental starter
pp 187–188

Advance Organiser

We are going to sort shapes into sets

You will need: 3-D shapes

Whole-class work

- Introduce or revise the term 'polyhedron' to describe shapes with *many faces*. Write it on the board. Ensure that the children can identify faces as the *flat surfaces* of 3-D shapes. Use a variety of examples of polyhedra to reinforce the definition.

- Ask the children to tell you something about a regular polyhedron.

- Write suggestions on the board and confirm that a *regular* polyhedron is a 3-D shape with many faces where all the faces are the same size and shape.

- Ask the children to select shapes that meet this criterion; for example, a cube, a tetrahedron, an octahedron. Ask the class to agree if it is or is not a regular polyhedron.

- Look at a square-based pyramid and a regular tetrahedron (a triangular-based pyramid).

- *What can you tell me about the faces of these shapes?*

- Draw a Venn diagram on the board as shown.

- Discuss each shape in turn and decide where it should be placed.

- Ask the children to write the names of the shapes in the correct sections. Encourage them to say whether or not they agree.

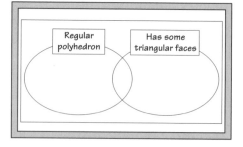

Independent, paired or group work

- In pairs, ask the children to take a selection of shapes and decide how to sort them. They can then record their sorting visually using sets drawn on paper, or record the names of the shapes in diagrams drawn in their books.

Plenary

- Select a property of 3-D shapes; for example, *shapes with at least one curved surface*.

- Show the children one shape that has that property and say *This is a ticket for the bus.*

- Children take turns to select a shape and ask if they can get on the bus.

- Tell the children if they can get on or not, but not why.

- Challenge the class to guess at each stage what the property is that gets them on the bus. Successful children get to choose the next property.

Recognising equilateral and isosceles triangles

Advance Organiser

We are going to name equilateral and isosceles triangles

Oral/mental starter pp 187–188

You will need: lots of different types of triangles for sorting

Whole-class work

- Ask a child to draw a triangle on the board. Look at the shape and ask the class if they agree that it is a triangle.

- *Is there a right angle? Are two or more sides the same length? Are two or more angles the same size? Are all three sides different? Are the sides all straight? Are there three vertices (corners)?*

- Draw on the board the shapes shown.

- *Are these triangles? How do you know?*

- Introduce or remind the children of 'equilateral' and 'isosceles' triangles. Ask the children to find those triangles and pass them around the class.

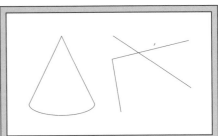

- Write on the board: *equilateral* and *isosceles*.

- Continue passing different triangles around the class, or showing or drawing larger triangles. Ask the children what sort of triangle each is, and how they know.

- You might want to introduce the word 'scalene' for triangles with three sides and three angles of different sizes.

- Point out that some right-angled triangles are also isosceles triangles.

- Point out that all equilateral triangles have two equal sides and two equal angles and are therefore also isosceles. Draw on the board this diagram to illustrate the relationship.

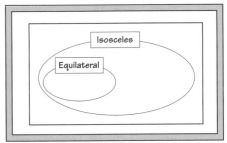

Independent, paired or group work

- Give the children a variety of triangles in their pairs or groups and ask them to sort them into different sets; for example, with or without a right angle, isosceles or not isosceles, and draw a Carroll diagram or similar to show this sorting.

Plenary

- Discuss all the ways to sort triangles.

- Ask the children to restate the reasons for placing a shape in a particular set.

- *Where would this triangle go in your sorting diagram? What about anyone else's diagram? What else can you tell me about this triangle?*

Using grids with numbered lines

Oral/mental starter
pp 187–188

Advance Organiser

We are going to use numbers to find points on a grid

You will need: resource page A (one per child and two enlarged), Blu-Tack

Whole-class work

- Use an enlarged copy of resource page A.

- *Who can tell me what this is?*

- Explain that the pairs of numbers are coordinates for a point. Ask a child to find the first point for shape 1 and mark it with an x where the lines cross. If necessary explain that the first number in a coordinate pair relates to the x-axis (horizontal) and that the second relates to the y-axis (vertical).

- Ask another child to find the next point and join the two points with a straight line.

- Ask another child to find the third point and join it to the other two points.

- *What is this shape?*

- Make shape 2 in the same way. Each time, join a new point to the previous one. Invite other children to find the points for shape 2 and join them. Complete the shape by joining the final point to the first one.

- If the children are confident, give them a sheet each and ask them to mark all the points and draw the shapes. If not, continue to complete the remaining shapes together.

- Use the small grids to draw more shapes and write the coordinates.

Independent, paired or group work

- Give the children each a copy of resource page A and ask them to draw the shapes.

- *Check with your partner that your shapes are the same. Discuss any differences with them.*

- *Use the first of the small grids to draw a shape and write the coordinates for the points.*

- *Read your coordinates to your partner to draw your shape without seeing it. Check the shape with your drawing. Now listen to your partner's coordinates and draw the shape. Ask your partner to check your shape.*

Plenary

- Play a treasure-hunt game using another enlarged copy of resource page A.

- Secretly choose the location of some 'treasure' and write it on the back of the sheet. Fix the sheet to the board with Blu-Tack.

- Ask the children to guess where the treasure is by giving coordinates.

- Ask the children to locate and mark each guess.

- Tell them whether they are 'hot', 'warm', 'cool' or 'cold' so that they can get closer to the correct location.

Name: _____

Points on a grid

Mark the points and join them up to make these shapes:

1 (2,1) (1,2) (4,2)
   are the corners of

   ....

2 (1,3) (1,5) (3,5) (3,3)
   are the corners of

   ....

3 (5,8) (4,7) (5,4) (6,7)
   are the corners of

   ....

4 (7,1) (6,2) (6,3) (7,4)
   (8,3), (8,2) are the
   corners of

   ....

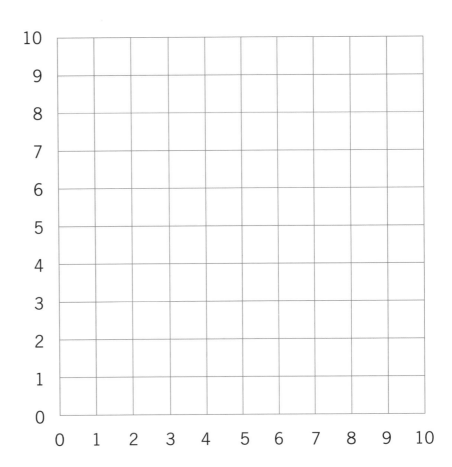

Join points on these grids to make shapes. Write the coordinates for each point.

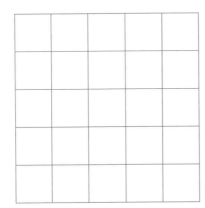

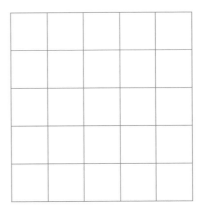

Classworks © Classworks Numeracy author team, Nelson Thornes Ltd, 2003

Investigating general statements about shapes

Advance Organiser

We are going to investigate the general statement, 'If you join the midpoints of any triangle you get four smaller, equal triangles'

Oral/mental starter pp 187–188

You will need: pencils, paper, rulers, resource page B (one per child and one enlarged)

Whole-class work

- Show the children an enlarged copy of resource page B.

- Demonstrate joining the midpoints of the first triangle to make four smaller triangles.

- *Look at each smaller triangle. What do you notice?*

- *How could we check that they are all the same?*

- Cut out the triangles and demonstrate that they are all (almost!) the same.

- *Will this happen with other triangles? Why do you think that?*

- Ask the children how they will test it.

- Encourage them to think about difficulties with accuracy and so on.

Independent, paired or group work

- Give the children copies of resource page B and ask them to investigate the statement.

- Each time, ask them to cut out the four small triangles and check that they are all near-identical in size and shape.

Plenary

- Discuss what you have found out.

- *Will the same procedure work for all shapes?*

- *Visualise what will happen with a square and a rectangle.*

- *Does it work for all quadrilaterals? What happens with a pentagon? A hexagon?*

Name: _____

Investigating triangles

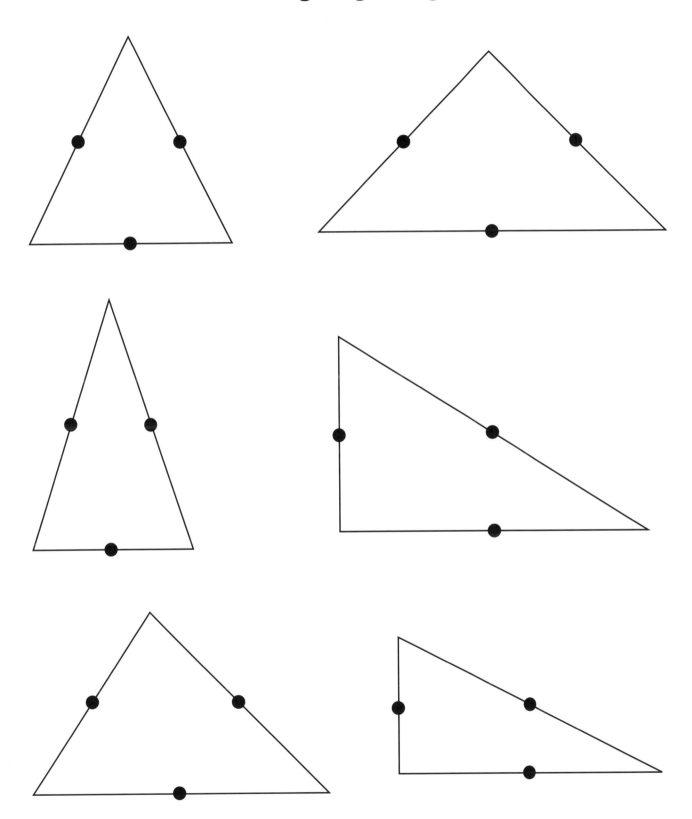

Shape and Space (2)

Outcome

Children will be able to identify simple nets, use positional and directional language and solve shape problems

Medium-term plan objectives	• Make shapes and discuss properties.
	• Visualise solid shapes from 2-D drawings.
	• Identify simple nets.
	• Recognise clockwise, anticlockwise.
	• Start to draw, measure and order angles.
	• Use eight compass points.
	• Recognise horizontal and vertical lines.
	• Solve shape problems or puzzles.
	• Explain reasoning and methods.
Overview	• Identify simple nets.
	• Recognise clockwise and anticlockwise.
	• Use eight compass points.
	• Shape problem: how many ways can you cut a rectangle in half?

How you could plan this unit

	Stage 1	Stage 2	Stage 3	Stage 4	Stage 5
	Identifying simple nets	Recognising clockwise and anticlockwise	Using eight compass points	How many ways can you cut a rectangle into two halves?	
Content and vocabulary	*shape, pattern, flat, line, curved, straight, hollow, solid, corner, point, pointed, face, side, edge, end, net, surface, base, triangle, square, rectangle*	*direction, clockwise, anticlockwise, movement, direction, far, further, furthest*	*north, south, east, west, north-east, north-west, south-east, south-west, N, S, E, W*	*centre, make, build, construct, draw, sketch, justify, make a statement, investigate, check*	
Notes		Resource page A	Resource page B		

Identifying simple nets

Advance Organiser

We are going to find out about nets of 3-D shapes

Oral/mental starter
pp 187-188

You will need: 3-D shapes, a set of empty cardboard boxes that are cubes and
cuboids, scissors, tape, unfolded Toblerone box, Polydron or Clixi

Whole-class work

- Show the children a large box, such as a Cornflakes box. Undo the glued edges and unfold the box to a flat net. Remove any overlaps.

- *We call this the 'net' of this box. It is how the box looks when we unfold it.*

- Ask the children to tell you the name of each face. Count the faces.

- Ask a child to fold the box again to show how the net becomes a box.

- Repeat for other different boxes until there are a few different nets at the front of the class.

- Ask the children to talk about the nets and think about what they will look like folded into boxes.

- Encourage the children to think about the shapes of the faces and their position in the net. Ask children to fold the nets back into boxes to see if what they predicted was correct.

- Show the children an unfolded Toblerone box.

- *What sort of shape will this make if I unfold it into a box? Why do you think that?*

- Write some suggestions on the board.

- *What can you tell me about the shapes in this net? Where will each shape be if I fold the box together?*

- Ask the children to help you fold up the net and stick it together.

- *Who is surprised? Why?*

Independent, paired or group work

- Give pair child a set of Polydron, Clixi or similar shape-making apparatus.

- Ask them to investigate making shapes using the apparatus. When each pair has made a few shapes, ask them to unfold the shapes so they are flat, and challenge another group to say what shape the net will be.

- They then fold up the shapes to check.

Plenary

- Use the box of 3-D shapes.

- Ask a child to pick up a shape and describe what the net might look like. They can sketch the net on the board if they prefer.

- Discuss each net with the class and check with Polydron or Clixi to see if the description was correct, nearly correct, or incorrect.

Recognising clockwise and anticlockwise

Advance Organiser

We are going to practise recognising clockwise and anticlockwise movement

Oral/mental starter pp 187–188

You will need: clock face with moveable but not geared hands, resource page A (one per child and one enlarged)

Whole-class work

- Show the children an enlarged copy of resource page A. Ask two children to each choose the name of a space station.

- Indicate the two space stations on the diagram.

- *Is it quicker to travel clockwise or anticlockwise between these space stations?*

- Repeat with other pairs of space stations.

- If necessary, demonstrate counting the number of stops to find the shortest route.

- Each time, ask the class to predict whether clockwise or anticlockwise is the better route and explain how they reached their decision.

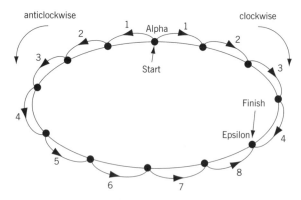

Independent, paired or group work

- Give each pair a copy of resource page A.

- Ask each child to make up six journeys and write them in a list like this: *Alpha to Gamma; Epsilon to Beta; Iota to Delta; Kappa to Theta and so on.*

- *Give your list to your partner.*

- The partner works out whether the quickest route is clockwise or anticlockwise. Write the word beside the journey.

Plenary

- Talk about the journeys the children considered.

- Ask the children to explain any strategies they used to remind themselves which direction was clockwise and which anticlockwise.

- *When was the largest difference between the anticlockwise and clockwise directions? When was the smallest difference?*

Name:

Space stations around Hellenos 5

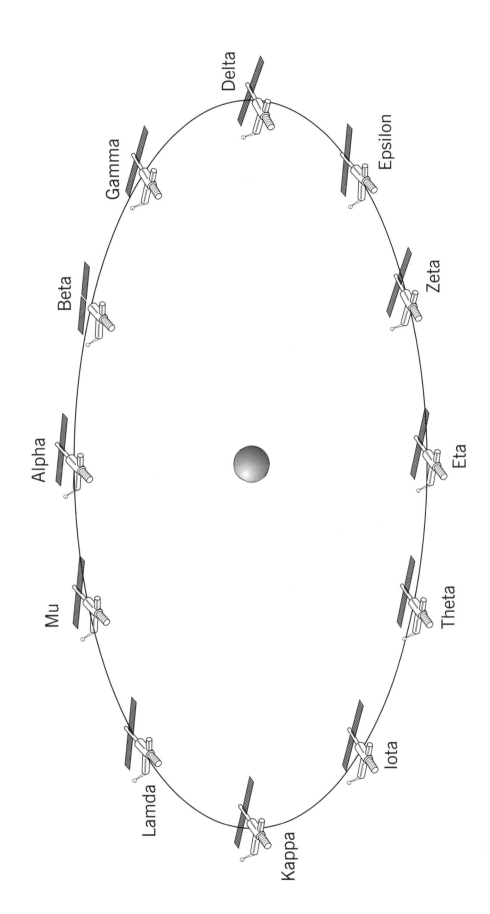

Classworks © Classworks Numeracy author team, Nelson Thornes Ltd, 2003

Using eight compass points

Advance Organiser

We are going to use eight points of the compass to describe directions

Oral/mental starter pp 187–188

You will need: resource page B (one per child and one enlarged), rulers

Whole-class work

- Draw the four points on the compass and label NESW. Draw the four intermediate, shorter lines.

- Point to the intermediate lines in turn.

- *Who can tell me what direction this is? Who knows what we should label this point?*

- Show the children how the new points get their names from the nearest points, NE is between N and E for instance.

- Ask the children to label the remaining points.

- Practise pointing in the new directions.

- Use the enlarged copy of resource page B. Choose the city nearest to your school.

- Ask the children to name places to the north of your city.

- *How do you know?*

- Repeat with the four main points. Find the names of places in each direction.

- Hold the page upside down.

- *Now which places are north of our city? Have they changed?*

- Repeat for east and west and confirm that whichever way you hold the map, the compass directions stay the same.

- Repeat for the intermediate compass points.

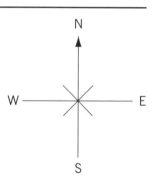

Independent, paired or group work

- Give each child a copy of the map on resource page B and a ruler.

- Ask the children to choose any *other* city. They should then draw and label the eight points of the compass at the top of the map.

- *Use the cities on the map to write a sentence for at least four compass points; for example, Glasgow is to the north of Carlisle, Edinburgh is to the north-east of Carlisle and so on.*

Plenary

- Ask the children to read out their sentences.

- Use the large copy of the map to check the statements.

- Check that everyone agrees.

Name: _____

Compass directions

How many ways can you cut a rectangle into two halves?

Advance Organiser

We are going to find out how many ways there are to cut a rectangle into two halves

Oral/mental starter pp 187–188

You will need: pencils, paper, rulers, scissors

Whole-class work

- Use some sheets of A4 paper. Ask a child to fold the paper into two halves. Cut along the fold and match the halves, one on top of the other.
- *Are these two parts exact halves of the whole rectangle? How can you tell?*
- Use another sheet and ask for a different fold. Again, cut the sheet along the fold and match the two pieces to check.
- Ask for one more way then cut and check.
- Cut the rectangle into two obviously unequal parts.
- *Have I cut this rectangle into two halves? Why do you think that?*
- *What do you notice about these halves? How are they different to the unequal parts?*
- Ask the children to discuss this and to think about how to predict whether a cut will produce halves.

Independent, paired or group work

- Give the children a sheet of identical rectangles (draw around a plastic shape for accuracy).
- Ask the children to record the ways you have already found by using a ruler to draw the lines on the rectangles.
- Ask them to find more ways, using their ruler to help them.
- Some children may prefer to cut out the rectangles, then fold them, cut and check.
- Others will be able to use measurement to draw lines that cut the shape into two halves.

Plenary

- Discuss what you have found out.
- If necessary, suggest to the children that the similarity between the cuts that halve a rectangle could be that they go through the centre of the rectangle.

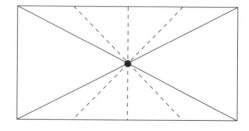

- Ask them if they think this is a rule, and if they think they could prove it.
- *So, how many different ways do you think we could do this?*
- Discuss the children's answers. The true answer is that any straight cut that passes through the centre and touches both sides will halve the rectangle. So there are an infinite number of possible cuts.

Shape and Space (3)

Outcome

Children will be able to draw reflections and describe translations, identify angles in degrees and use the vocabulary of movement

Medium-term plan objectives

- Sketch reflections of simple shapes in a mirror.
- Read, and begin to write, the vocabulary of movement.
- Make and describe patterns involving translation.
- Begin to measure degrees.
- Know whole turn, 360 degrees, four right angles, quarter turn, 90 degrees, one right angle, half turn, 180 degrees, two right angles.
- Recognise that 45 degrees is half a right angle.

Overview

- Reflections in a mirror.
- Make and describe patterns involving translation.
- Know 360 degrees is four right angles, 180 degrees is two right angles, 90 degrees is one right angle, 45 degrees is half a right angle.
- Begin to use the vocabulary of movement.

How you could plan this unit

	Stage 1	Stage 2	Stage 3	Stage 4	Stage 5
	Reflections in a mirror	Patterns involving translation	Compass points, degrees and right angles	Reading and writing the vocabulary of movement	
Content and vocabulary	*mirror line, reflection, reflect, match, symmetrical*	*translation, pattern, repeating pattern*	*compass point, north, south, east, west, north-east, north-west, south-east, south-west, N, E, S, W, NE, NW, SE, SW, angle, right angle, degree*	*left, right, up, down*	
Notes	Resource page A				

Reflections in a mirror

Advance Organiser

We are going to predict and draw reflections in a mirror

You will need: mirrors, squares and rectangles (or more complex shapes whose angles are right angles), Blu-Tack, rulers, resource page A (one per child)

Whole-class work

- Choose one of the 2-D shapes. Fix it to the board with Blu-Tack. Draw a mirror line.

- *Imagine this line is a mirror line. What shape will appear on the other side of the line?*

- Ask the children to suggest answers. Give them mirrors and allow them to look at the reflections of similar shapes.

- Ask the children to volunteer to draw the reflection of the shape on the board.

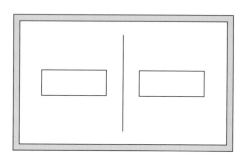

- Use a ruler to check that the vertices of the rectangles are an equal distance from the mirror line.

- Point out that every part of the rectangle has a 'matching' point on its reflection that is the same distance from the mirror line.

- Repeat with other shapes, keeping the mirror line parallel to one side of the shape. Use more complex shapes as the children grow more confident.

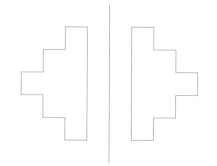

- Each time, ask the children whether the reflection is correct and demonstrate checking with a ruler.

Independent, paired or group work

- Give each child a copy of resource page A, a pencil and a ruler.

- Ask the children to use the ruler to draw the reflected shapes accurately.

- If you are working in a group, show the children how to measure and locate key points of the shape. Expect all straight lines to be drawn with a ruler, not freehand.

- Praise the children for accurate measurement.

- Quick finishers can draw a mirror line down the centre of the back of the sheet and design more shapes for others to add the reflections.

Plenary

- Ask some children to show the class their drawings. Use mirrors to check for accuracy. Praise accurate measurement and drawing.

Name: _____

Drawing reflections

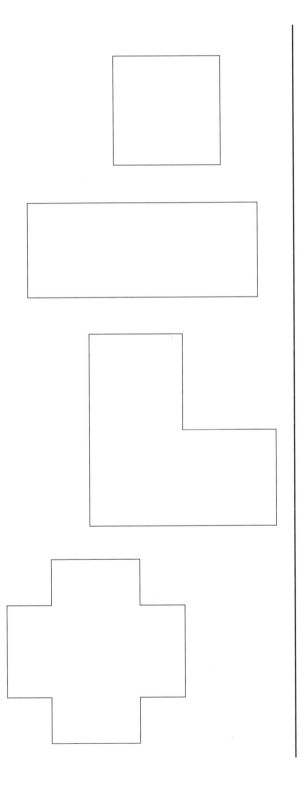

Patterns involving translation

Oral/mental starter
pp 187–188

Advance Organiser

We are going to make patterns using translations

You will need: 2-D shapes to draw around

Whole-class work

- Draw around a rectangle on the board. Ask the children to imagine that a line of rectangles of exactly the same size and shape are tiles.

- *What shape or pattern will a line of tiles make?*

- Describe the pattern, then ask a child to draw around the shape to make a line of translated rectangles on the board.

- Write on the board: *translation*.

- *When a shape pattern is made by moving the same shape in the same direction by the same amount each time, we say we have translated the shape. It is a translation pattern.*

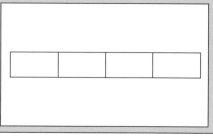

- Turn the rectangle through 90 degrees and draw around it underneath the original outline.

- *Will the tile make the same translation pattern now? How would you describe it?*

- Ask a child to draw around the rectangle to continue the pattern.

- Choose another tile and ask the children to predict the pattern it would make in a line.

- Ask someone else to draw around the shape to show the translation pattern.

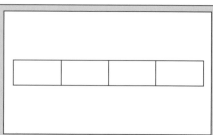

- *Was the prediction correct?*

- *How does the pattern change if we turn it through 180 degrees? Is it the same, or different? What will it look like?*

- Repeat these questions for different patterns, including those which will have different patterns when turned 180 degrees and those which will be identical.

Independent, paired or group work

- Ask the children to choose a 2-D shape and to make a pattern by translating the design along the line.

- They can design their own more complex pattern if they wish, but all designs must be translated.

Plenary

- Discuss the patterns created.

- *Were there any surprises? Explain why you thought that.*

Compass points, degrees and right angles

Advance Organiser

We are going to use compass points to work out angles

You will need: rulers, paper and pencils

Whole-class work

- Draw the four points of the compass. Ask the children to help you label them NSEW.

- Draw the four intermediate lines and ask the children to tell you how to label them.

- Ask them to tell you the angle between north and east.

- Confirm that the angle is 90 degrees, or *one right angle.*

- *Look at the angle between north and north-east. What is half of 90?*

- Confirm that the angle is 45 degrees, or *half of one right angle.*

- Ask the children to help you mark all the angles that are 45 degrees.

- *If I was facing north and I turned to face south, what angle would I turn through?*

- Ask the children to give you suggestions. Demonstrate by turning yourself around and by indicating the marked angles. Add the intervening angles if necessary.

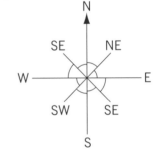

- *Who can work out the number of degrees in a clockwise turn from north to west? Which other turns would be 270 degrees?*

Independent, paired or group work

- Ask the children to draw a compass and mark the eight compass points on it.

- Challenge them to write down where they will be facing if they start at North each time and take: three turns of 45 degrees, three of 90 degrees, three of 180 degrees, and three of 360 degrees. Ask them to write down the compass points involved, the number of degrees, and how many right angles that is. For example, *north to south, 180 degrees, two right angles.*

Plenary

- Ask the children to read out one of their turns without saying how many degrees it is. Challenge the class to say how many degrees. Ask them to say how many right angles as well – some may work out the degrees from the right angles and others may calculate the right angles from the degrees.

- Use the diagram on the board to check that the angles and directions are correct. Use a ruler to show the angles and the directions as you check each statement.

Reading and writing the vocabulary of movement

Advance Organiser

We are going to describe a pattern so that our partners can make an identical one

You will need: dotted paper, pencils

Oral/mental starter pp 187–188

Whole-class work

- Draw several rows and columns of dots on the board to simulate dotted paper, or use an enlarged sheet of dotted paper.

- Place your pen on a dot near the centre and turn yourself so you are facing the board or clipboard in the same way as the children. Tell the children you are going to be a robot and they have to tell you what to do.

- They can ask you to move right, up, down or left.

- Ask the children in turn to suggest a move and draw the pattern.

- Repeat until several children have had a turn.

- Give each child a sheet of dotted paper. Read out to them the directions to make the pattern you have just drawn on the board.

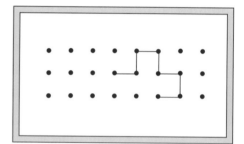

- Allow them to look at the board for reference, if necessary.

- When they have finished, compare their in patterns with the original.

- Repeat the exercise from the beginning, this time using compass directions (draw a compass on the board to begin with) and allowing moves in each of the eight directions.

Independent, paired or group work

- Now tell the children they are going to work in pairs. One child will draw a pattern, one line at a time, and describe it to their partner. Without looking, the partner will try to follow the instructions. They repeat for five or six lines then compare their patterns.

- Allow the children to use *either* right, left, up and down *or* compass directions, but not both.

Plenary

- Ask the children to say their sequences without showing you.

- Follow the instructions to draw the pattern on the board.

- Compare it with the children's patterns.

- *Is it the same? If not, were the instructions difficult to follow, or did you make a mistake?*

Handling Data (1)

Outcome

Children will be able to solve problems by collecting, classifying, representing and interpreting data in tally charts, frequency tables and pictograms

Medium-term plan objectives

- Solve a given problem by collecting, classifying, representing and interpreting data in tally charts, frequency tables, pictograms – symbols representing 2, 5, 10 units.

- Include use of computer.

Overview

- Collect data by tallying, recording on frequency tables and making pictograms.

How you could plan this unit

	Stage 1	Stage 2	Stage 3	Stage 4	Stage 5
Content and vocabulary	Would you rather? *count, tally, sort, vote, survey, questionnaire, data, pictogram, represent, most popular, least popular, most common, least common*	Traffic survey	Pictograms with symbols representing ten units		
Notes	Resource pages A and B	Resource pages C and D	Children can combine the previous traffic survey data to show total traffic, using a symbol to represent ten units. As a follow-up activity, put the data into a simple spreadsheet using Excel, or similar, on a computer. Highlight the data and let the children experiment with the Chart Wizard.		

Would you rather?

Advance Organiser

We are going to find out 'what we would rather do' by making a pictogram

Oral/mental starter p 188

You will need: resource page A (one per child and one enlarged), resource page B (enlarged)

Whole-class work

- Tell the children they are going to choose what they would rather do from three unpleasant options. Then they are going to find a way to decide on the whole class's choice and display their information.

- *Would you rather: have a bath full of worms, spend a day with baked beans in your socks or eat a chocolate-covered grasshopper?*

- After they have discussed the options for a short while, ask them how we could find out and display what the whole class would rather do.

- *How could we record our votes and count them?*

- If no one suggests it, show the children how to tally in fives to make counting and recording quicker and easier.

- One way to remember it is that each five is a handful: four fingers then the thumb going across diagonally. Alternatively, the tally can be described as a 'barred gate'.

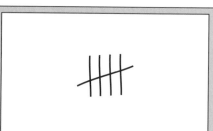

- Look at an enlarged version of resource page A and give each child their own copy.

- Ask the children, in turn, what they would rather do, pausing so that they can all insert a tally mark in the correct place on their activity sheet.

- When an option's score reaches 5 make sure they insert the diagonal 'thumb' or 'bar'.

- When the data is collected, count together in fives and write the value for each option in the *Number* column.

- Look at the sample pictogram on resource page B and ask questions about it.

- Draw out that it has a title, that the symbols are arranged in columns and rows, and that the symbols are of equal width.

- Make sure that the children understand the use of half a symbol to represent one.

Independent, paired or group work

- Ask the children to draw a pictogram in their books using the data they have collected.

Plenary

- Look at a selection of the children's pictograms.

- *Which is the most popular option?*

- *Which is the least popular?*

- *Is this an easy way to compare the data?*

Name: _____

What we would rather do

Would you rather?	Tally	Number
Have a bath full of worms		
Spend a day with baked beans in your socks		
Eat a chocolate-covered grasshopper		

Make a pictogram using this data and draw it using the axes below.

Name: _____

Our lunch time options

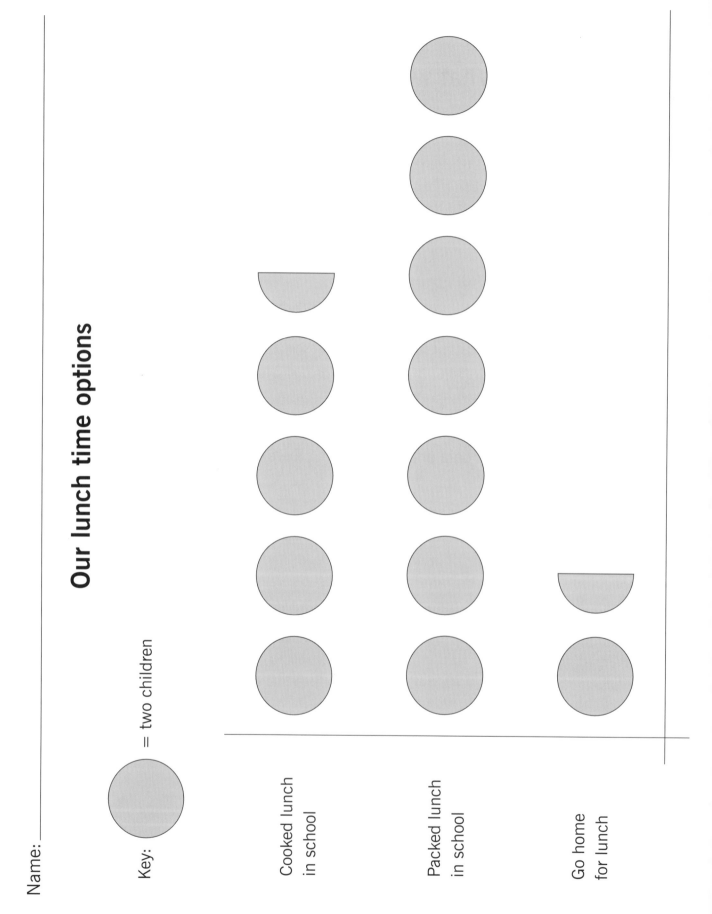

Key: = two children

Cooked lunch
in school

Packed lunch
in school

Go home
for lunch

Traffic survey

Advance Organiser

We are going to investigate traffic in our local area

Oral/mental starter p 188

You will need: resource page C (one per child and two enlarged) and resource page D (one per child)

Whole-class work

- This activity requires that you have the opportunity to conduct a traffic survey with the class.

- You will need to follow the appropriate safety guidelines.

- Prior to carrying out the survey, pose a hypothesis that you think there is more traffic travelling in one direction than in the other.

- *We are going to carry out a survey to see if we are right.*

- One possible way of regulating the duration of the survey is to stop after the fiftieth car.

- Give the children each a copy of resource page C and discuss the different sorts of traffic.

- Point out that you all need to agree on the difference between a bus and a lorry, and a car and a van, and so on, so that your data will be accurate.

- Revise tallying with the children, if necessary.

- Half of the class should look at traffic going in one direction and the other half at traffic going in the other direction.

- Following the survey, use two enlarged versions of resource page C to collate agreed data for both directions of traffic.

- *How many bicycles did you record? Did anyone record anything different?*

- *Why do you think that is? What shall we agree is the most accurate total?*

- Discuss using the total most agreed upon, or the number halfway between two differing totals.

Independent, paired or group work

- Ask the children to draw a pictogram on resource page D using the data collated.

- They can decide for which direction they are recording the data.

- Ask the children to begin by looking at the key.

- *One symbol means five vehicles.*

- Discuss how to adapt the symbol to approximate for *less than five vehicles.*

Plenary

- Look at a selection of pictograms.

- *Which type of vehicle was the commonest in each direction?*

- *How can we compare our pictograms?*

- *Which direction of traffic was busier overall?*

- *Are pictograms a good way of comparing traffic?*

Name: _____

Our traffic survey

Type of vehicle	Tally	Number
Bicycles and motorcycles		
Cars		
Vans and trucks		
Lorries (6 wheels or more)		
Buses, coaches and minibuses		

PUPIL PAGE

Name: _____

Key: = 5 vehicles

Handling Data (2)

Outcome

Children will be able to read different scales and use the information to solve problems

Medium-term plan objectives	• Solve a given problem by collecting, classifying, representing and interpreting data in bar charts – intervals labelled in units of 2, 5, 10 and 20. • Include use of computer.
Overview	• Read and interpret graphs labelled in units of 2, 5, 10 and 20. • Draw graphs labelled in units of 5 and 10.

How you could plan this unit

	Stage 1	Stage 2	Stage 3	Stage 4	Stage 5
Content and vocabulary	House points *label, title, axis, axes, scale, division*	Traffic survey *survey, questionnaire, data, graph, block graph, represent, bar chart*	Computer charts		
Notes	Resource page A	Resource pages A and B	As a follow-up activity, put the data from a previous activity into a simple spreadsheet using Excel, or similar, on a computer. Highlight the data and let the children experiment with the Chart Wizard.		

House points

Advance Organiser

We are going to look at, and interpret, two bar graphs

Oral/mental starter p 188

You will need: resource page A (one per child and one enlarged)

Whole-class work

- Compare the two graphs on an enlarged version of resource page A.

- Ask about different areas of the graph.

- Draw out essential features such as the titles, the labelled scale 'Number of house points' on the y-axis and the labelled data fields 'classes' ('Class 1', 'Class 2' and so on) on the x-axis.

- Point out that both charts are the same size, but that the scales have been drawn differently.

- Use the board to demonstrate how to read odd-numbered values from a scale marked in twos.

- Now draw a scale marked and labelled in fives and demonstrate how to read values that are not multiples of 5.

- For example, 9 and 11 are just below and just above 10; 2 and 3 are just below and just above the halfway point between 0 and 5; 4 and 6 are just below and just above 5; 7 and 8 are just below and just above the halfway point between 5 and 10.

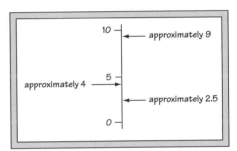

Independent, paired or group work

- Ask the children to complete resource page A.

- They should answer their questions in their books.

Plenary

- Check through some of the answers.

- *Which chart was easier to read? Why?*

- *Which chart scale would be easier to use if the totals were much larger?*

- Have a look at a selection of the children's drawn charts.

- Check that their charts have a title, and labelled x- and y-axes.

(PUPIL PAGE)

Name: _____

House points

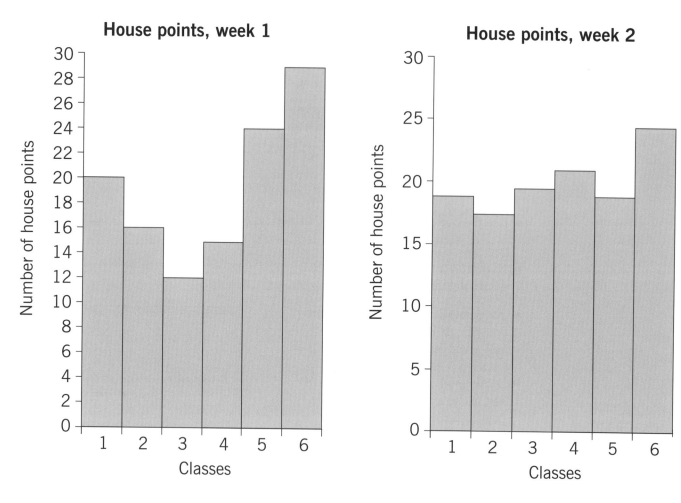

Look at the two charts and find the answers to these questions.

1 How many house points did each class get in week 1?

2 How many house points did each class get in week 2?

3 **(a)** Which classes improved their total in week 2?

(b) How many did they improve by?

4 **(a)** Which classes had fewer house points in week 2?

(b) What is the difference between their week 1 and week 2 totals?

5 List the totals for week 1 in order, starting with the class which had the highest total.

6 List the totals for week 2 in order, starting with the class which had the highest total.

7 Draw a new bar chart for week 1, numbering the scale in fives every two squares.

Classworks © Classworks Numeracy author team, Nelson Thornes Ltd, 2003

Traffic survey

Advance Organiser

We are going to look at, and interpret, two bar graphs

Oral/mental starter
p 188

You will need: squared paper, resource page A (enlarged), resource page B (one per child and one enlarged)

Whole-class work

- Look at an enlarged version of resource page B and compare it to the enlarged version of resource page A.

- Point out that the charts all have a title and two labelled axes.

- Look at the different scales and size of the numbers involved.

- Draw out what is easier and harder about reading from a chart with large intervals.

- Point out that the 20-minute chart is harder to read accurately and that the readings will have to be approximate.

- It is possible to represent larger numbers on a small chart.

- Go through how to set out the chart specified as task 5 on resource page B.

- The scale on the *x*-axis should be marked off at one square intervals in tens.

Independent, paired or group work

- Ask the children to complete resource page B.

- If they are using squared paper exercise books marked in 10 mm squares, they will need to use a double page to draw the required chart.

Plenary

- Check through some of the answers.

- *Which chart was easier to read? Why do you think that?*

- *Which chart scale would be easier to use if the totals were much higher?*

- Have a look at a selection of the children's drawn charts.

- Ask the class to check that their have a title, and labelled *x*- and *y*-axes.

(PUPIL PAGE)

Name: _____

Traffic survey

A school counted the traffic for 10 minutes, then started again for another 20 minutes. They made two bar charts.

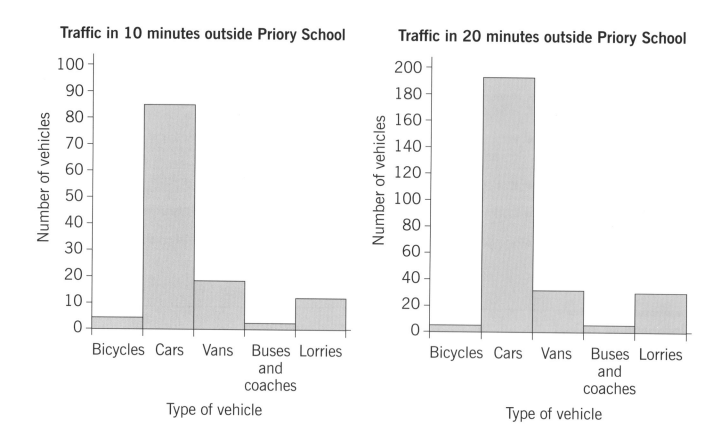

Traffic in 10 minutes outside Priory School

Traffic in 20 minutes outside Priory School

Look at the charts and find the answers to these questions.

1   How many bicycles, cars, vans, buses and coaches, and lorries passed the school in the first 10 minutes?

2   Approximately how many bicycles, cars, vans, buses and coaches, and lorries passed the school in the next 20 minutes?

3   Which vehicle numbers were more than double for 20 minutes what they were for 10 minutes?

4   Which were less than double for 20 minutes what they were for 10 minutes?

5   Draw a new graph for the 20-minute survey. Mark the scale every square in tens.

Handling Data (3)

Outcome

Children will be able to solve problems using Venn and Carroll diagrams for two criteria

Medium-term plan objectives	• Solve a given problem by collecting, classifying, representing and interpreting data in Venn and Carroll diagrams – two criteria. • Use a computer and a branching-tree program to sort shapes or numbers.
Overview	• Read and create Venn diagrams to solve problems. • Read and create Carroll diagrams to solve problems. • Compare the same data on two diagrams.

How you could plan this unit

	Stage 1	Stage 2	Stage 3	Stage 4	Stage 5
Content and vocabulary	Venn diagrams *Venn diagram, label, title, group, set*	Carroll diagrams *Carroll diagram*	Computer sorting		
Notes	Resource page A	Resource page B	Use a branching-tree program with the data from this unit, and ask children to discuss the differences between the ways of sorting.		

Venn diagrams

We are going to use a Venn diagram to classify some animals

Oral/mental starter p 188

You will need: resource page A (one per child and one for you)

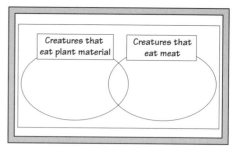

Whole-class work

- Draw a universal set and two Venn diagram rings on the board, labelling them as shown.

- *Who can tell me what this is? Who knows what it is called? What does it tell me?*

- Draw out that the diagram is a Venn diagram.

- *Who can help me to complete the diagram?*

- Point to the 'Creatures that eat plant material' section.

- *Who can think of something to go here?*

- Ensure the children understand that only the names of creatures that eat plant material belong in this set.

- Repeat for creatures that eat meat. Use the examples on resource page A if you like.

- Discuss whether some creatures eat only plants, only meat or plants and meat.

- *What about badgers? They eat meat and plants. Where shall I write 'badger'?*

- Continue to fill in names on the diagram until the children have all grasped the idea.

- *Where could I write 'daffodil'?*

- Draw out that a daffodil is not a member of either set within the diagram.

- Write *daffodil* outside the rings but inside the universal set.

Independent, paired or group work

- Ask the children to complete resource page A.

- They need to fill in the rest of the names on the Venn diagram, then answer the questions.

Plenary

- Ask the children where a human would normally be placed on the Venn diagram (bearing in mind those humans who choose not to eat meat or animal products).

- *How many of the animals in the Venn diagram are omnivorous?*

- *Which is the smallest/largest herbivore?*

- Go over some of the children's answers and discuss, with the class, where to place the animals.

Name: _____

What do they eat?

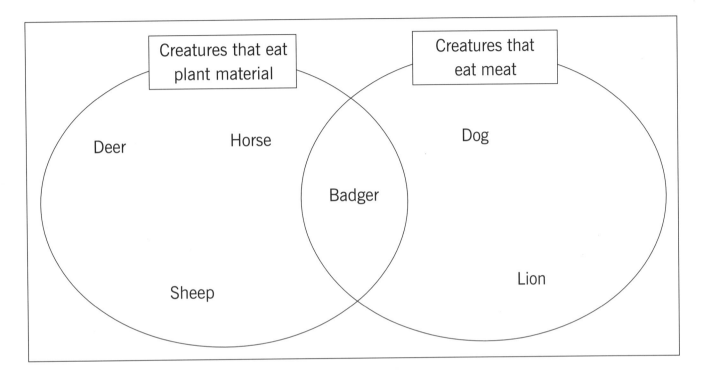

Creatures that eat only plant material are called *herbivores*.
Creatures that eat only meat are called *carnivores*.
Creatures that eat both plant material and meat are called *omnivores*.

Write these animals' names in the correct places on the Venn diagram.

Herbivores: aphid, elephant, giraffe, koala
Carnivores: cheetah, hyena, seal, weasel, wolf
Omnivores: ant, chimpanzee, cockroach, fox, grizzly bear, seagull

Answer these questions in your book.
1 Which of the animals eat meat?
2 Which of the animals eat plant material?
3 Which herbivore are you most likely to find in your garden?
4 Which omnivore are you most likely to find in your garden?
5 Which of the carnivores are you most likely to have as a pet?
6 Which herbivore is most likely to be found on farms?
7 Which of the carnivores prefers fish?
8 Which omnivore flies?

Classworks © Classworks Numeracy author team, Nelson Thornes Ltd, 2003

Carroll diagrams

Oral/mental starter
p 188

Advance Organiser

We are going to use a Carroll diagram to classify ourselves

You will need: resource page B (one per child)

Whole-class work

- Make a list of the children's names on the board and put their age at the side, plus whether they are a boy or a girl.

- Ask a couple of difficult questions relating to the list.

- *How many boys are in the class?*

- *How many of you are 8 years old?*

- Encourage the children to think of ways of better presenting the information.

- *How could we organise our information to make it easier to answer these questions?*

- Once a few ideas have been suggested, draw this Carroll diagram grid on the board.

- *Can anyone tell me anything about this chart?*

- *Does anyone know its name?*

- *How is it similar to a Venn diagram?*

- *How is it different?*

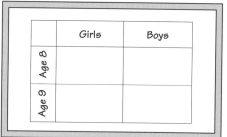

- Draw out that each person can only appear in one region; each criterion is an *either/or* choice; the name goes in the region which is in both the correct row and the correct column.

- Point out that there are four regions in the Carroll diagram.

- Compare the Carroll diagram to the Venn diagram on the enlarged resource page A, which also has four regions: each set, the overlapping area and the universal set.

- Ask one or two children to suggest where their names should go on the Carroll diagram and why.

- Agree the answers with the class.

Independent, paired or group work

- Ask the children to complete resource page B in their books.

Plenary

- Check through the answers to the questions on resource page B with the class.

- Look at a selection of children's Carroll diagrams.

- Write up a Venn diagram on the board using the same information.

- *What is clearer on the Venn diagram? What is clearer on the Carroll diagram?*

Name: _____

Children in our class

	Girls	Boys
Age 8		
Age 9		

Use the Carroll diagram to answer these questions.

1 How many boys are in the class altogether?

2 How many children are in the class altogether?

3 How many of you are 8 years old?

4 How many girls are 8 years old?

5 How many girls are there altogether?

6 How many boys are 9 years old?

7 How many of you are 9 years old?

8 Write some other questions you could answer using this Carroll diagram.

Fractions (1)

Outcome

Children will be able to recognise and use fraction notation and relate fractions to division

Medium-term plan objectives	• Use fraction notation. • Recognise fractions that are several parts of a whole, and mixed numbers. • Find fractions of shapes. • Relate fractions to division, and find simple fractions of quantities.
Overview	• Colour and write non-unit fractions of shapes. • Make and name fractions of shapes which are greater than one whole. • Find fractions of quantities of objects and measurements by dividing into equal parts.

How you could plan this unit

	Stage 1	Stage 2	Stage 3	Stage 4	Stage 5
Content and vocabulary	Non-unit fractions of shapes *part, equal parts, fraction*	Mixed numbers *improper fraction, mixed number*	Fractions and division *equivalent to*		
Notes		Resource page A	Resource page B		

166

Non-unit fractions of shapes

Advance Organiser

We are going to shade $\frac{3}{5}$ of a whole shape

Oral/mental starter
p 184

You will need: A4 sheet of paper, squared paper

Whole-class work

- Hold up a paper rectangle (an A4 sheet of paper). Fold it in half, then in half again.
- *How many parts do you think there will be when I open this out?*
- *The rectangle is divided into how many equal parts?*
- *What is each part called?*
- Write $\frac{1}{4}$ on each part.
- Draw a rectangle on the board and divide it into four equal parts. Colour one of them.
- Stress that the '4' represents four equal parts and the '1' represents the one part that is coloured.
- Fold the rectangle so that two of the four parts are showing.
- Have a pupil colour in another part on the rectangle on the board.
- Write $\frac{2}{4}$ beside it. Continue colouring $\frac{3}{4}$ and $\frac{4}{4}$.
- Fold another rectangle into quarters and then eighths. Open it out.
- *Count the parts. Each is called $\frac{1}{8}$.*
- *What does 8 mean in this fraction? What does the 1 mean in this fraction?*
- Confirm that out of the 8 parts in the whole rectangle, each eighth is 1 of them.
- Repeat the process of colouring eighths – $\frac{2}{8}$, $\frac{3}{8}$, $\frac{4}{8}$ and so on – and discussing how to write that fraction of the whole rectangle.

Independent, paired or group work

- Using 2 × 2 grids on squared paper, ask the children to colour and label the grids to show $\frac{1}{4}$, $\frac{2}{4}$, $\frac{3}{4}$ and $\frac{4}{4}$.
- Using 2 × 4 grids on squared paper, ask the children to colour and label the grids to show $\frac{1}{8}$, $\frac{2}{8}$, $\frac{3}{8}$ and so on to $\frac{8}{8}$.
- Write a number of non-unit fractions on the board and ask the children to draw appropriate shapes, such as shown below, and shade these fractions: $\frac{2}{3}$, $\frac{2}{4}$, $\frac{3}{4}$, $\frac{2}{5}$, $\frac{3}{5}$, $\frac{3}{8}$, $\frac{5}{8}$, $\frac{7}{8}$.

Plenary

- Draw a diagram on the board of a shaded shape, illustrating fractions such as $\frac{3}{5}$.
- *What fraction of the whole shape is shaded?*
- *What does the 5 mean in the fraction $\frac{3}{5}$?*
- *What does the 3 stand for?*

Mixed numbers

Advance Organiser

We are going to investigate making shapes using six-quarters of a whole rectangle

Oral/mental starter p 184

You will need: Clixi or Polydron, A4 paper, resource page A (one per child), linking cubes, OHP

Whole-class work

- Show the children two A4 sheets of paper, each folded into quarters and opened out.

- *How many quarters are there in a whole rectangle? How many in two whole rectangles?*

- Write $\frac{1}{4}$ on each quarter. Demonstrate cutting each sheet into four sections and joining them back together to make two whole sheets.

- *How could we record this?*

- Write on the board: $1 = \frac{4}{4}$ and $2 = \square$.

- Encourage children towards the answer $2 = \frac{8}{4}$.

- *What does this mean? What does the 8 tell us? What about the 4?*

- *How many whole rectangles like this could we make if we only had 6 quarter-rectangles?*

- Ask the children to the front of the class to demonstrate making rectangles using only six of the quarters.

- *How could we record this?* Introduce the notation and terms used.

- *6 quarter-rectangles make 1 rectangle and 1 half rectangle.* $\frac{6}{4} = 1\frac{1}{2}$.

- Introduce the term 'mixed number' to describe a value made up of whole numbers and fractions. Describe $\frac{6}{4}$ as a top heavy or improper fraction.

- Some pupils will recognise that $\frac{6}{4} = \frac{3}{2}$. Encourage this informal noting of equivalence.

- Provide each child with apparatus in which the hexagons can be divided into sixths; for example, Clixi or Polydron.

- *Show a way of making a fraction greater than 1 whole but less than 2 wholes, using the sixths.*

- *Repeat this process several times.*

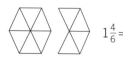

$1\frac{4}{6} = \frac{10}{6}$

Independent, paired or group work

- Ask the children to complete resource page A.

Plenary

- Go over the examples from resource page A.

- Revise the idea, using linking cubes on an OHP representing mixed numbers such as $1\frac{3}{4}$, where each cube represents $\frac{1}{4}$. *How many quarters are there in one whole? How many quarters are there altogether?*

- Write $1\frac{3}{4} = \frac{7}{4}$. Try other examples, as appropriate.

Name: _____

Mixed numbers

Write the mixed numbers below each fraction.

1

....

2

....

3

....

4

....

5

....

6

....

Classworks © Classworks Numeracy author team, Nelson Thornes Ltd, 2003

Fractions and division

Advance Organiser

We are going to divide a number of cubes into equal parts and write the answer as a fraction

You will need: linking cubes, OHP (optional), resource page B (one per child)

Oral/mental starter p 184

Whole-class work

- Give pairs of children four linking cubes each.

- Place four cubes on an OHP.

- *How would I divide this many cubes into two halves or equal groups?*

- Ask the children to share out their cubes equally.

- *What fraction of the whole number of cubes is each share?*

- Note the difficulty here of seeing the cubes as the whole amount when discrete objects are being used. Share the four cubes between two and each share is one half of the total number of cubes. Illustrate this using the cubes on the OHP.

- *Finding one half of the cubes is the same as dividing by 2.*

- Write on the board: $\frac{1}{2}$ *of 4 = 2 and* $\frac{4}{2} = 2$.

- Repeat with different numbers of cubes on the OHP until the idea that sharing between two will enable the children to find one half of the amount.

- Ask the children to draw number lines 12 centimetres (cm) long.

- *How would we find the point halfway along the line?*

- *Finding* $\frac{1}{2}$ *of the line is the same as dividing the line into two equal parts.*

- Write on the board: $\frac{1}{2}$ *of 12 cm = 6 cm. 12 cm ÷ 2 = 6 cm.*

- Demonstrate measuring 6 cm from one end and marking this point on the line.

6 cm

- Draw a line 6 cm long and ask the children to help you divide it into three equal parts; then try lines of 9 cm and 12 cm, making clear each time the link between the fraction and the division.

Independent, paired or group work

- Ask the children to complete resource page B.

Plenary

- Make a tower with 12 cubes and have a pupil show how it can be shared equally between four people.

- Review the fact that dividing the cubes equally, between four, will mean that each person gets three, and three is $\frac{1}{4}$ of 12.

- Revise writing: $\frac{12}{4} = 3$. $\frac{1}{4}$ *of 12 is 3.*

Name: _____

Fractions of lengths

Using a ruler, draw lines the following lengths and mark the fractions of each one.
Write what you have found. The first one has been done for you.

1 Find $\frac{1}{5}$ of a line 10 cm long.

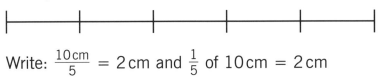

Write: $\frac{10\,cm}{5} = 2\,cm$ and $\frac{1}{5}$ of 10 cm = 2 cm

2 Find $\frac{1}{3}$ of a line 12 cm long.

....

3 Find $\frac{1}{4}$ of a line 12 cm long.

....

4 Find $\frac{1}{6}$ of a line 12 cm long.

....

5 Find $\frac{1}{10}$ of a line 20 cm long.

....

6 Find $\frac{3}{4}$ of a line 8 cm long.

....

Fractions (2)

Outcome

Children will be able to identify equivalent fractions, compare fractions and use decimal notation

Medium-term plan objectives	<ul><li>Recognise equivalence of simple fractions.</li><li>Identify two fractions with a total of 1.</li><li>Compare a fraction with one-half, and say whether it is greater or less.</li><li>Use decimal notation for tenths, hundredths (money, metres and centimetres), and use in context.</li><li>Round to the nearest pound or metre.</li><li>Convert pound to pence, or metres to centimetres, and vice versa.</li><li>Order decimals with two places.</li></ul>
Overview	<ul><li>Recognise equivalent fractions of shapes through the use of fraction walls and game formats.</li><li>Colour fractions of one whole and write the remaining fraction.</li><li>Relate decimal notation for tenths and hundredths to money and the measurement of length using a 10 × 10 grid to illustrate.</li><li>Order decimals involving tenths and hundredths as applied to the measurement of height.</li></ul>

How you could plan this unit

	Stage 1	Stage 2	Stage 3	Stage 4	Stage 5
Content and vocabulary	Equivalent fractions *equivalent to*	Fractions that add to make one whole *one whole, part, equal parts*	Decimal notation of money *money, pound, pence, £, ones, tens, place, place value, tenth, hundredth, decimal point, decimal, decimal place, decimal fraction*	Ordering decimal fractions *greater than, less than, ascending/descending order, between*	
Notes	Resource page A			Resource page B	

Equivalent fractions

Advance Organiser

We are going to find fractions the same value as one-quarter

Oral/mental starter p 184

You will need: cubes or counters (per pair), 1 to 6 die (per pair), resource page A (one enlarged per child)

Whole-class work

- With the children, build up a fraction wall on the board.

- Ask the children to suggest different fractions of a whole that are equivalent.

- *How many quarters in one whole? How many sixths? How do you know?*

- When the wall is complete up to, for example, twelfths, ask questions about equivalent fractions.

one whole			
$\frac{1}{2}$		$\frac{1}{2}$	
$\frac{1}{4}$	$\frac{1}{4}$	$\frac{1}{4}$	$\frac{1}{4}$
$\frac{1}{8}$ $\frac{1}{8}$	$\frac{1}{8}$ $\frac{1}{8}$	$\frac{1}{8}$ $\frac{1}{8}$	$\frac{1}{8}$ $\frac{1}{8}$

- *How many halves are equivalent to one whole? How many quarters are equivalent to one-half? How many sixths are equivalent to one-third?*

- Ask the children to identify a fraction, then challenge others to list all the equivalent fractions they can think of.

Independent, paired or group work

- Children play a game using a die numbered 1 to 6 and cubes or counters.

- Give each child a copy of the fraction wall on an enlarged version of resource page A.

- In pairs, they take turns to throw the die and place that number of cubes on the row of sixteenths on the fraction wall, one on each sixteenth.

- When there are two-sixteenths covered, they exchange these cubes for one to be placed on an eighth.

- Similarly, when two-eighths are covered, then exchange those cubes for one to be placed on a quarter.

- The person who wins is the first one to place a cube on the *one whole* section at the top of their fraction wall.

Plenary

- Refer to the fraction walls on the board showing one, halves, quarters, eighths and sixteenths, and one, thirds, sixths and twelfths.

- Question the children in order to create sets of equivalent fractions.

Name:

Fraction wall

1				
$\frac{1}{2}$	$\frac{1}{4}$	$\frac{1}{8}$	$\frac{1}{16}$	
			$\frac{1}{16}$	
		$\frac{1}{8}$	$\frac{1}{16}$	
			$\frac{1}{16}$	
	$\frac{1}{4}$	$\frac{1}{8}$	$\frac{1}{16}$	
			$\frac{1}{16}$	
		$\frac{1}{8}$	$\frac{1}{16}$	
			$\frac{1}{16}$	
$\frac{1}{2}$	$\frac{1}{4}$	$\frac{1}{8}$	$\frac{1}{16}$	
			$\frac{1}{16}$	
		$\frac{1}{8}$	$\frac{1}{16}$	
			$\frac{1}{16}$	
	$\frac{1}{4}$	$\frac{1}{8}$	$\frac{1}{16}$	
			$\frac{1}{16}$	
		$\frac{1}{8}$	$\frac{1}{16}$	
			$\frac{1}{16}$	

Fractions that add to make one whole

Advance Organiser

We are going to say the fraction added to tenths to make one whole

Oral/mental starter
p 184

You will need: counting stick with ten divisions, sticky labels

Whole-class work

- Use a counting stick with ten divisions and labels noting fractions from $\frac{1}{10}$ to $\frac{10}{10}$ and 1.

- Go over the fractional parts of the stick.

- Point to $\frac{1}{10}$.

- How many more tenths are there altogether on the whole stick?

- Write $\frac{1}{10}$ on a sticky label.

- Discuss how this could be written and write on the board: $\frac{1}{10} + \frac{9}{10} = \frac{10}{10}$ *or 1 whole.*

- Continue with other fractions; for example, $\frac{3}{10}, \frac{5}{10}, \frac{7}{10}$ asking how many more tenths there are altogether.

- Write up the addition in each case.

- Draw a fraction strip divided into tenths on the board or OHP.

- Cover a number of tenths at various points on the strip. For example, cover one-tenth near the middle of the strip.

- How many more tenths are there in the whole strip?

- Record each time that the two fractions of the whole strip added together equal one whole.

- Repeat this teaching sequence with a strip divided into four equal parts, then five equal parts.

Independent, paired or group work

- Ask the children to draw rectangles or part-rectangles on centimetre-squared paper, and then to shade a fraction of the shape and challenge their partner to say how much is left unshaded.

- Write sentences for each shape.

Plenary

- Go over the questions from the activity, writing out some of the addition sentences the children have made and discuss them.

- Ensure pupils are aware that there are $\frac{6}{6}, \frac{7}{7}$ and so on in one whole.

Decimal notation of money

Advance Organiser

We are going to write amounts of money using decimal notation

Oral/mental starter
p 184

You will need: a 1 to 100 grid, facsimile coins (£1, 10p and 1p)

Whole-class work

- Write on the board: *3.25.*
- *Who can tell me about this number?*
- Where have you seen a number like this before?
- Confirm that this is a decimal number with the dot (point) separating the whole numbers from the parts or fractions of 1.
- Write on the board: *£3.25.*
- *What is the value of the 3, the 2 and the 5 in this number?*
- Confirm that the 3 stands for whole pounds and the 25 for pence, or parts of a pound.
- *How many pence are there in one pound?*
- Stress that there are 3 whole pounds and 25 pence in £3.25.
- Introduce a grid with 100 squares made from squared paper.
- *The grid has 100 squares and represents £1.00. What would one square be worth? What about ten squares?*
- Write the following on the board to represent numbers of pence (p): *£0.01, £0.02, £0.10* and so on.
- *If the whole grid is £1, how much of the grid is 25p?*
- Point out that 25p is $\frac{25}{100}$ or 25 small squares on the grid.
- *How do we write this as money?*
- Confirm that this can be written as £0.25 in money or 0.25.

Independent, paired or group work

- Using a number of facsimile coins worth £1, 10p and 1p, ask the children to make groups of coins and write each one as a sum of money in decimal notation.

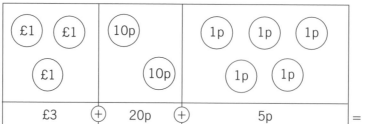

- They should also draw their coins in a table each time.

Plenary

- Ask the children to suggest sums of money. Challenge others to say how many £1, 10p and 1p coins would be worth the same as that sum of money.
- Ask the children to suggest different contexts in which decimal notation is used.
- Introduce metres and centimetres as another example.

Ordering decimal fractions

Advance Organiser

We are going to say which is greater, 1.22 or 1.36

Oral/mental starter
p 184

You will need: height chart or metre rules, or strips of graph paper to measure children's height, Blu-Tack or sticky tape, resource page B

Whole-class work

- Using a height chart for up to 2 m, measure the heights of six pupils in metres and centimetres. (Attach a metre rule to the wall one metre off the ground or use strips of graph paper stuck to the wall.)

- *How tall is Jobeda? How do we record that as a decimal?*

- Write on the board: *1 m 22 cm* and *1.22 m*.

- List the heights of six children in random order in decimal form and ask pupils to order them from the shortest to the tallest.

- Ask for ideas of how to do this. Ensure that they realise they should apply place value principles to the heights as they are in decimal form.

- Draw a 1 m to 2 m number line on the board.

- *Who can tell me where I should mark 1.3 metres? What about 1.5 metres? How can we work it out?*

- Mark in the points 1.1, 1.2, 1.3, 1.4 and so on, linking these with the measurements, 1 m, 10 cm and so on.

1m   2m

- What is 1.6 m in metres and centimetres?

- If necessary, draw a place value chart to confirm that 1.6 m is 1 m 60 cm, rather than 1 m 6 cm.

- *Where can we mark our six heights on this line?*

- Discuss the position and order of the numbers.

- *Hannah is 1.45 m tall. Where should I mark this on the line?*

- Discuss this with the children. Ensure that they are clear that *1.45* is *more than 1.4* and *less than 1.5*.

Independent, paired or group work

- Ask the children to complete resource page B.

Plenary

- Go through the examples from resource page B with the children.

- Ask them to describe how they answered each question.

- Some may have used number sequences to predict the missing numbers.

Name: _____

Ordering decimals

Use a number line to help you write these decimals in order.

Fill in the spaces:

| 1.12 | 1.13 | 1.14 | _____ | 1.16 | 1.17 | _____ |

| 1.25 | 1.26 | 1.27 | _____ | 1.29 | _____ | 1.31 |

| 1.04 | 1.05 | 1.06 | 1.07 | _____ | _____ | 1.10 |

| 0.03 | 0.04 | 0.05 | _____ | 0.07 | _____ | 0.09 |

Write the following numbers in order from greatest to least value.

| 1.51 | 1.06 | 1.1 | 1.04 | 1.25 | |

| 1.6 | 1.09 | 1.45 | 1.58 | 1.3 | |

| 1.9 | 1.88 | 1.56 | 1.37 | 1.77 | |

| 0.1 | 0.05 | 0.02 | 0.09 | 0.01 | 0.07 |

Fractions (3)

Outcome

Children will be able to identify simple proportions and equivalent decimal fractions

Medium-term plan objectives	• Begin to use ideas of simple proportion.
	• Recognise the equivalence of decimal, fraction forms of one-half, one-quarter and tenths.

Overview	• Write statements about the ratio and proportion of two quantities of objects.
	• Shade a 10×10 grid to show the relationship between the fractions $\frac{1}{2}$, $\frac{1}{4}$ and $\frac{1}{10}$ of the grid and the corresponding decimal fraction, and write these equivalences.

How you could plan this unit

	Stage 1	Stage 2	Stage 3	Stage 4	Stage 5
Content and vocabulary	Ratio and proportion *in every, for every, proportion*	Equivalent fractions and decimals *part, equal parts, decimal, decimal fraction, decimal point, decimal place*			
Notes	Resource page A				

Ratio and proportion

Oral/mental starter p 184

Advance Organiser

We are going to work out how many red cubes for every green cube

You will need: six linking cubes (two red, four green, per child), counters in red and green (per pair), resource page A (one per child)

Whole-class work

- Give the children six linking cubes each, two of which are red and the others green.
- *Make a rod starting with a red cube, then place two green, a red and two green.*
- *For every one red cube, how many green cubes are there?*
- *For every two green cubes how many red cubes are there?*
- Ensure that the children understand the language. Encourage them to make statements about the cubes such as: *For every red cube, there are two green cubes. One in every three cubes is red. Two in every three cubes is green.*
- In pairs, give children six counters: two red and four green.
- *Start sharing out the counters by giving one red one to your partner and keeping two green ones yourself. For the one red counter you have given away you have kept two green counters.*
- Do this again with the remaining red counter.
- *For every one red you have given away, you have kept two green ones.*
- Have the children put the six counters together again.
- *One in every three is red and two in every three is green.*
- Display a strip of card/paper divided into six equal sections – one blue for every two yellow.
- Write on the board the statement: *For every ONE _____ part there are _____ yellow parts.*
- *Help me to complete this statement.*
- Write on the board the statement: *For every TWO _____ parts there is _____ blue part.*
- *Help me to complete this statement.*
- Write on the board the statement: *There is _____ blue part in every _____ parts.*
- *Help me to complete this statement.*
- Practise the use of this language with other examples, as necessary.

Independent, paired or group work

- Children complete resource page A.

Plenary

- Go through resource page A with the children.
- Review the statements using the linking cubes, as above.

180

PUPIL PAGE

Name: _____

Ratio and proportion

Complete the statements next to each set of sweets.

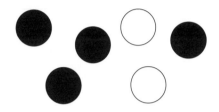

1 For every _____ white there are _____ black sweets.

For every _____ black there is _____ white sweet.

One in every _____ sweets is white.

_____ in every 3 sweets are black.

2 For every _____ black there are _____ white sweets.

For every _____ white there is _____ black sweet.

One in every _____ sweets is black.

_____ in every _____ sweets is white.

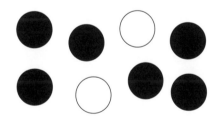

3 For every _____ white there are _____ black sweets.

For every _____ black there is _____ white sweet.

One in every _____ sweets are black.

_____ in every _____ sweets is white.

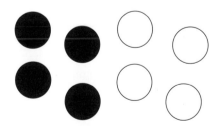

4 Write out your own statements for this example.

Classworks © Classworks Numeracy author team, Nelson Thornes Ltd, 2003

Equivalent fractions and decimals

Advance Organiser

We are going to write one-tenth as a decimal fraction

You will need: 10 × 10 square grids (per child), OHP if available

Whole-class work

- Demonstrate using a 10 × 10 grid on an OHP.

- Give each child a copy of a 10 × 10 grid.

- Shade one-tenth of this grid.

- *How could we write this as a fraction? How else could we write it? How many hundredths have I shaded?*

- Write the various forms on the board.

- Relate to money if necessary: $\frac{1}{10}$ *of £1.00 is 10p or £0.10.*

- Insert 0.10 into a calculator and press '=' to see that 0.10 = 0.1.

- Continue with $\frac{2}{10}$ = 0.2 and so on until you reach 0.5 = $\frac{5}{10}$.

- *What fraction of the grid has been shaded?*

- *How many hundredths of the grid has been shaded?*

- Write on the board: $\frac{1}{2}$, *0.5*, $\frac{50}{100}$ and $\frac{5}{10}$.

- Continue with tenths from $\frac{6}{10}$ to one whole.

- Establish that $\frac{100}{100}$ is the same as $\frac{10}{10}$ as they are both equivalent to one whole.

- Using an enlarged 10 × 10 grid, ask the children to direct you to divide it into four equal parts.

- *What fraction is each part? How many squares are there is in each quarter?*

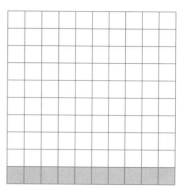

$\frac{1}{10}$ **is equivalent to** $\frac{10}{100}$

which is equivalent to 0.1

Independent, paired or group work

- Give each child a few 10 × 10 square grids.

- Ask the children to work in pairs. Write some tenths fractions on the board. In turn, children secretly choose a fraction, shade a grid to match it, then swap sheets and challenge their partner to identify which fraction they have shaded.

Plenary

- Review the fractions $\frac{1}{2}$, $\frac{1}{4}$ and $\frac{1}{10}$, asking pupils to state the equivalent common and decimal fraction.

- Write up the equation in each case; for example, $\frac{1}{10} = \frac{10}{100} = 0.1$, $\frac{5}{10} = \frac{50}{100} = \frac{1}{2}$ = 0.5 and so on.

- Establish that any fraction written in tenths or hundredths may be changed readily to a decimal fraction.

Oral/mental starter ideas

Properties of number

How many tens/hundreds?

Write a start number on the board, or say it aloud to the children; for example, 37. *How many tens will we have to count to get past 100?* Repeat for other numbers. Extend, to starting from 259 and saying how many hundreds to pass 1000.

In-between bingo

Ask the children to write down nine four-digit numbers of their choice. Call out *Between 1491 and 1523* and so on, and write it on the board. If the children have a number between those two numbers, they can cross it out. The first to finish says *Bingo!* You can check using the record you kept on the board.

Is it in the sequence?

Start a sequence and ask the children to join in when they know the rule; for example, count in fours from 113, count in twenty-fives from 50, count back in fives beyond 0 from 25 and so on. After the children have all or mostly joined in, stop the count and ask: *Will 328 be in the sequence? Will 134? Who agrees? How do you know that 750 is in the sequence? What comes after 10, 5, 0 ...?*

Multiples

Call out *multiples of 10, multiples of 2, multiples of 3, multiples of 4* and so on, and ask the children to name one in turn. They keep going around the circle as long as they can manage. Alternatively, write a mixed set of numbers on the board and ask the children which is not, for example, a multiple of 4, and how they know.

Negative numbers

Ask a variety of negative-number problems. For example, count up and down across zero, then write a set of positive and negative numbers on the board and ask the children to help you order them. Extend to simple addition and subtraction calculations, for example, *What is three more than minus two?* and so on.

Rounding

Tell the children you are going to ask them to round some numbers. Revise the fact that, for example, 450 is rounded up to 500. Call out numbers and look for the correct responses from the class. Repeat, for time to the nearest hour, or nearest 10 seconds, minutes and so on. Alternatively, write an addition or subtraction on the board, such as 806 + 997, and ask the children which approximation is closest to the real answer, rounding to the nearest 10 (810 + 1000 = 1810) or to the nearest 100 (800 + 1000 = 1800) and why they think that is.

Estimating

Draw a number line on the board and number each end; for example, 0 and 100, or 500 and 1000. Point to positions on the line and ask children to estimate the value.

Fractions

Fractions of...

Ask questions involving fractions of whole numbers or quantities, for example, $\frac{1}{4}$ of 16, $\frac{1}{8}$ of 24, $\frac{1}{10}$ of 500, $\frac{1}{2}$ of 100, $\frac{1}{5}$ of 35, $\frac{1}{3}$ of 300 ml, $\frac{1}{6}$ of 666 cm.

Fraction equivalences

Call out a less familiar form of a simple fraction, such as $\frac{2}{4}$, $\frac{5}{10}$, $\frac{2}{6}$ and so on. Ask the children to say other equivalent fractions. Continue around the circle, each child saying a new equivalent fraction. Alternatively, call out various fractions, such as $\frac{3}{4}$, $\frac{2}{3}$, $\frac{2}{5}$, $\frac{3}{7}$ and so on, asking the children to say more or less than one-half.

Fraction and decimal line

Draw a number line on the board and number the ends 0 and 1. Point to positions on the line and ask the children to estimate their value. If necessary, add dividers to show, for example, half or quarters. Repeat using decimal notation.

Decimal rounding

Call out a decimal number, such as 3.6, and ask the children to say the value of each digit. Repeat for other numbers, then ask the children to round the number to the nearest whole number, revising the fact that, for example, 3.5 is rounded up to 4. Alternatively, write a group of decimal numbers on the board and ask the children to help you order them from least to greatest value, or vice versa.

Addition and subtraction

Number bonds

Choose a target number between 0 and 20. Going around the circle, each child has to give a pair of number bonds for that number. Reversals are fine but anyone who repeats exactly a pair already used is 'out'. Alternatively, one child calls out one number, for example, 17, and the next has to call out its bond to the target number. Repeat with bonds to 100, or pairs of multiples of 50 that add to make 1000.

How many more?

Write a target number on the board such as, for example, 3603. Call out a smaller number the other side of a hundreds boundary, 2897, and ask how many more to make the target number. Change the numbers and repeat. Alternatively, write a small difference, such as 43, on the board, and say a number just less than a hundreds number; for example, 3789. Children have to add the difference to find the new number.

9, 11, 19, 21...

Ask questions adding or subtracting 9, 19, 29 and so on or 11, 21, 31 and so on; for example, $14 + 29$, $56 - 31$ and so on. Show a 1 to 100 grid as support if necessary, pointing down the columns as you ask the questions, or asking children to the front to demonstrate using the grid or to describe how to use the grid.

Multiplication and division

Phrasing

Ask a mixture of multiplication and division questions using different phrasing; for example, *Share 20 between 4. Divide 16 by 2. What's half of 24? How many fives in 25? What's 5 times 6? Multiply 8 by 3. Two lots of 9 makes ...? Is 45 a multiple of 9? What's the product of 7 and 8? Name a factor of 42.*

Times-tables

Practise children's two, three, four, five and ten times-tables, chanting each as a class. Then ask a mixture of rapid questions involving different tables. *What is 2 times 4? What is 5 times 4? What is 10 times 4? What is 3 times 8? What is 4 times 6? What is 8 multiplied by 10?*

Mental or written?

Ask one child to think of a two-digit number. Ask another child simultaneously to think of a number between 1 and 9. The class then decide if they can find the product in their heads or on the board. Discuss how to solve the equation; for example, 11×5 or 23×3 might be calculated quickly using a mental method, whereas 27×8 might be better with a written method. After a few goes, discuss what sorts of calculation are best done with each method. Include discussions about how different children might prefer to use different methods for the same calculation.

Remainders

Ask the children a mixture of division questions, some of which require answers to be given with remainders. Discuss quick ways of working these out; for example, working out $41 \div 4$ by rounding 41 down to 40 and showing the remainder of 1 lot of 4. Alternatively, include some rounding in context; *Boxes of eggs hold six eggs each. How many boxes do I need to hold 38 eggs? How many full boxes are there?*

Make it easy!

Write a 'difficult' calculation on the board; for example, 16×24, 15×19 and so on. Ask the children to suggest how to make it easier; for example, doubling 24 repeatedly, and multiplying 15 by 20 then adjusting. Solve the problem as a class.

Check it

Ask one child to solve a mental calculation, such as $245 + 39$, and to say the answer. Ask for a volunteer (or select a child) to check this calculation and explain how they are checking it. Continue with other children and other calculations.

Solving problems

Bees knees

Ask some word problems involving different animals or insects and how many legs they have; for example, *How many legs on 16 spiders? What about 24 badgers? How many on 38 ants? And so on.*

Explain it

Ask a variety of mental questions to individual children. Every so often, stop and ask a child to explain how they knew the answer, and to describe their method.

How much/how many?

Ask the children some money questions involving how many of something they can buy with a certain sum of money; for example, *How many books for £4.99 each can Ben buy with £20? How many children can go swimming at £1.10 each for £10? If pizzas cost £9.10 each, how much will seven cost altogether?* Extend to asking how much change in each case from a certain sum.

Money fractions

Ask some questions involving fractions of amounts of money; for example, *John spends one quarter of his money. He started with £8. How much does he have now? Becky has half as much as Selim. How much does she have if Selim has £12?*

General statements

Write a general statement on the board; for example, *the sum of the digits of a multiple of 9 is always 9.* Ask the children to suggest examples that illustrate this statement. Alternatively, ask children in groups to decide how to explain in words to someone how to work out how many days there are in a number of weeks.

How many questions?

Ask the children, for example, to find as many ways as possible of making each number from 1 to 40 using the digits 1 to 9 once only, with certain mathematical operators, such as just + and =, or + or × and =, and so on.

Find the numbers

Challenge the children to find two numbers with, for example, a sum of 20 and a product of 99, a sum of 20 and a product of 75, and so on. Alternatively, investigate the products of as many pairs of numbers with sum of 20 as they can. Can they find the largest and smallest products for a certain sum?

Measures

How long until...?

Ask some time questions using different ways of writing or saying times, such as, *How long from twenty-five past eight until half past nine? How long from two forty-three until four seventeen? How long from a quarter past three until three thirty-four? How many days from Tuesday 4th of March to Thursday 13th March? How many weeks and days from 3rd August to 15th September?*

Recipe

Write a simple recipe on the board; for example 100g flour, 40g butter, 20g sugar, 30ml water, and state that the recipe is for four people – how could the children make enough for eight people? What if the recipe was for two people – how could they make it enough for six people?

Sensible measures

Give the children some options of heights, weights, lengths, capacities and so on that they might encounter – which are the most sensible? For example, *Would you expect a person to be 2 metres tall, 3 metres tall or 9 feet tall? What unit would you use to measure the length of: a football field; the distance from Bristol to Manchester; the weight of an elephant or a feather; the capacity of a thimble?*

Equivalences

Ask some equivalence questions; for example, *how many minutes in an hour? How many seconds in a minute? One week is how many days?* Alternatively, write *60* ☐ *in 1* ☐ and ask for ways of filling the gaps. Repeat for amounts of metres and centimetres, kilos and grams, litres and millilitres, and so on. As a class, work out how many months in one year, how many weeks in one year, how many days, hours, minutes and seconds in one year. You can also play a 'what's more' game involving imperial and metric units; for example, *What has the greater mass, a book with a mass of 200 grams or a book with a mass of 1 pound?*

Shape and space

Clues for shapes

Revise definitions of familiar 3-D shapes. Ask the children to describe a cylinder, a cube, cuboid, prism, and so on. They take turns to describe a shape, then say the name of a person who has to find the right shape in a set of 3-D shapes; for example, *Find a shape with a square base and triangular faces.*

Triangle facts

Brainstorm a list of facts about triangles; for example, *They have three sides, they have three angles, some triangles are symmetrical, some triangles have right angles,* and so on. Name structures where you see triangles; for example, pylons.

Points on a grid

Draw a 10 by 10 grid on the board. Ask a child to say two numbers between 1 and 10; for example, 4 and 8. Write the pair of numbers (4,8) to show how coordinates are written. Show the children where to find 4 on the horizontal axis and 8 on the vertical axis. Trace both lines until you find the point where they cross. Mark the point with a colour. Ask another child to say two numbers between 1 and 10. Ask that child to choose someone else. That person finds the point on the grid.

General shapes

Brainstorm general statements about shapes; for example, opposite sides of a parallelogram are parallel, all the points on the surface of a sphere are an equal distance from its centre, all the angles of a square are right angles, and so on. Check, asking the children, to draw or pass around shapes that the statements are true.

Shape quiz

Revise naming 3-D shapes. Have a quick quiz. Hold up a shape and ask the children to name it. Repeat, this time asking them to say the number of faces. Repeat, this time asking the children to say the shape of the faces.

Clock numbers

Draw a large circle on the board. Ask different children to each write one number to make a clock face. The child may choose the number to write. Then, starting at 12, ask a child to draw an arrow to show the journey of the hour hand around the clock. Ask them to draw other familiar dials; for example, the speedometer of a car, a petrol gauge. *Where is zero? Which numbers are around the edge? How does the hand move? Is it a clockwise or an anticlockwise direction?*

Compass points

Mark the wall or corner of the classroom that is closest to north with a large capital N. Revise the four compass points. Ask the children to point to south, east and west. Discuss ways to remember which way round east and west are; for example, when writing the compass points, west and east spell 'we'. The four compass points in clockwise order follow the mnemonic 'Never Eat Shredded Wheat'. Make up another.

Mirror shapes

Ask two children to stand at the front, facing each other. Ask one child to use arms and legs to make a letter of the alphabet; for example, X, Y, F, I, K, R, T. Ask the other child to make the mirror image. Decide whether each shape is a mirror image.

Shape translations

Draw a 2-D shape on the board; for example, an isosceles triangle. Ask the children if they know what to draw if the shape is translated to the right. Write the word 'translations' on the board. Ask a volunteer to continue the line of translated shapes; for example as shown.

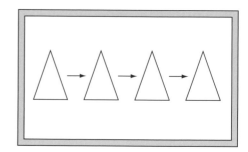

Repeat with other 2-D shapes.

Arms and angles

Ask the children to use two arms to make a right angle. Ask another child to make a different angle. Ask the class to estimate the angle and discuss what they say. Ask them to tell you how to make a 180 degree angle, then a 90 degree angle.

Lines

Revise the terms *horizontal*, *vertical* and *diagonal*. Look for vertical lines in the classroom; for example, the upright edges of the window, the corners of the room. Look for horizontal lines; for example, edges of surfaces. Ask the children to explain 'diagonal' by drawing the diagonals of squares and pentagons, and so on. Establish that diagonals are internal lines joining two corners of polygons.

Handling data

Favourites

Write a question on the board; for example, *Do we prefer watching sport, cartoons or soap operas on television?* Ask the children how they can decide, and how they can record the decision. Progress to making a table, using sets, bar charts and so on. Discuss the features of the chosen graph such as labels, scales, keys, and so on.

Venn and Carroll diagrams

Decide on some mathematical criteria that will make a Venn and Carroll diagram, such as numbers with a 9 digit, and multiples of 9. Record these with the children's help on Venn and Carroll diagrams and discuss the ways the data are presented. Repeat for, shapes with right angles and shapes with less than four sides.